Accessing...

Science

Teacher Resource Book

Year 6

Christine Moorcroft

Acknowledgements

United Kingdom: Folens Publishers, Apex Business Centre, Boscombe Road, Dunstable, LU5 4RL
Email: folens@folens.com

Ireland: Folens Publishers, Greenhills Road, Tallaght, Dublin 24
Email: info@folens.ie

Poland: JUKA, ul. Renesansowa 38, Warsaw 01-905

Editor: Chris Affleck
Layout artist: Patricia Hollingsworth
Illustrations: Paul Stanway and Chris Affleck
Cover design: Martin Cross
Cover image: CORBIS/Kevin Schafer

First published 2005 by Folens Limited.
Every effort has been made to contact copyright holders of material used in this publication. If any copyright holder has been overlooked, we should be pleased to make any necessary arrangements.

British Library Cataloguing in Publication Data. A catalogue record for this publication is available from the British Library.

ISBN 1 84303 565 0

Contents

Introduction

Folens *Accessing... Science Books* provide a collection of visual resources around which teachers can plan lessons based on the QCA schemes of work for the Foundation Stage and Key Stages 1 and 2.

Accessing... Science Books are a unique resource, which can provide every child in the class with high-quality visual material. It can be used as a starting point for whole-class or group discussions, or for individual work.

The *Big Books* and pupil *Photo Books* contain no text apart from captions and, occasionally, images which contain text. This makes the series a versatile resource which can be used by children with very different reading abilities. It also allows the maximum use of space for useful source material.

Accessing... Science Books are intended to be used by teachers to supplement their school's scheme of work rather than as a complete scheme in themselves.

Big Books and pupil *Photo Books* for **Science** include photographs and illustrations of items which the children might not otherwise have the opportunity to see; although their learning will be enriched if they also have the chance to experience some of these: people, animals, plants, places, materials, scientific phenomena and even scientists and their experiments and investigations.

The use of *Big Books* and multiple copies of *Photo Books* enables whole classes or groups of children to use the pictures to help them to complete tasks suggested in the *Teacher Resource Books*.

The *Teacher Resource Books* are designed to help busy teachers, who cannot be expected to be experts in every subject, to prepare interesting and motivating science lessons. They provide:

- ❑ background information for teachers
- ❑ vocabulary lists
- ❑ starting points
- ❑ suggestions for individual and group discussions and activities based on the visual resources
- ❑ discussion points for plenary sessions
- ❑ ideas for extensions for able children and support for less able children.

Additional activities are provided in the photocopiable pages.

Foundation Stage and Key Stage 1
The material for each of these age groups comprises:

Foundation Stage and Year 1
- ❑ a 20-page *Big Book*
- ❑ four A4 card copies of each poster from the *Big Book* which can be used flexibly: for example, for display or for groups or individuals to use as a stimulus for written or practical work or for reference
- ❑ a *Teacher Resource Book* supplying ideas for lessons and photocopiable activity sheets providing information, stories and activities

Year 2
- ❑ a 24-page *Big Book*
- ❑ a 48-page *Photo Book*
- ❑ a 64-page *Teacher Resource Book*

Key Stage 2
The materials for these age groups comprise:

- ❑ a 48-page *Photo Book* for each year group
- ❑ a 64-page *Teacher Resource Book* for each year group

Accessing... Science presents the materials and information which teachers need in order to follow the QCA schemes of work for Science and the Curriculum for the Foundation Stage (Knowledge and understanding of the world). Authors who know the subjects have done the necessary background research for the teacher.

Interdependence and adaptation

1 All kinds of leaves (1)
2 All kinds of leaves (2)

Photo Book reference Pages 4 and 5

QCA links

The children learn that green plants need light in order to grow well and that they make new plant material, using air and water in the presence of light. They learn that for this to take place, the plant needs leaves. (QCA Unit 6A)

Background information

Leaves are classified according to whether they are simple or compound, and according to their arrangement. A simple leaf might have lobes but no separate leaflets. A compound leaf has two or more leaflets. The epidermis (the outermost layer of cells on a leaf) has cells which secrete cutin, a waxy substance which forms a thin, waterproof layer. There are pores in the epidermis, through which gases can pass. The inner layer of a leaf contains veins and the cells which produce chlorophyll, the pigment which enables photosynthesis to take place. During photosynthesis, chlorophyll molecules absorb energy from sunlight and use it to provide fuel for the production of sugars and other carbohydrates. Leaves are the main sites for photosynthesis.

Deciduous trees shed their leaves in winter because they cannot produce food when there is little sunlight or the weather is cold. The trees become dormant and survive on stored food. The leaves of evergreens are able to continue producing food through the winter. The waxy coating of leaves such as holly and rhododendron helps them to survive the winter. Conifer leaves take the form of needles, which are also tough enough to survive the winter.

Starting point

■ Review the children's previous learning about plants. They will have studied local habitats and begun to notice the characteristics which help them to distinguish between plants. *What do they know about leaves?* Ask them if all plants have leaves. *Can they think of a plant (including trees, grasses, bushes) which never has leaves?* If they name mushrooms, point out that mushrooms are classed as fungi and that scientists class these separately from green plants. Many cacti and a few other plants (for example, mosses, liverworts and horsetails) have no leaves.

Using the pictures

❑ Ask the children if these plants have leaves. *Can they see any similarities between the leaves in the pictures, and between these and the leaves of other plants?* They could compare them with other familiar plants, houseplants around the school or plants in and around the school grounds. All these plants have green leaves, but the leaves have different formations, shapes, textures and arrangements.

❑ Use the picture to explain the difference between simple and compound leaves. All these plants, except asparagus, have simple leaves. Ask the children to look for other differences: for example, the shape of the leaves. Help them to ask questions to help them to distinguish between the leaves: *Are the leaves shiny or matt? Do they have a waxy surface? Are they furry on one, or both, sides? Do they have veins? Do the leaves have different colours or different shades of green?* (Introduce the term *variegated*.) *Are they round, long, narrow, wide, pointed, serrated, spiky, wavy-edged, smooth-edged? Do they grow singly, in pairs along the stem or in a rosette?*

Activities

● The children could collect other leaves and use what they have learned from the pictures to classify the leaves: for example, simple/compound, long/short, large/small, pointed/rounded, and so on. In addition to using leaves to help in classifying and identifying plants, the children could find out how the leaves are suited to the habitats of the plants: for example, do some leaves retain water, survive cold weather, strong sunlight or dark conditions better than others?

● Ask them if they think plants can survive without leaves. They could investigate what happens when they remove the leaves from a plant. Compare plants of the same kind and similar sizes; take photographs or make sketches of the plants each week, and measure the heights of the main stems; notice if they change colour or begin to wither.

● The children could find out how warmer temperatures affect leaf and flower buds of trees and bushes. In the winter, bring in twigs from plants, such as willow and forsythia, and put them in water. Compare their growth with that of the same buds outdoors.

Interdependence and adaptation

1 All kinds of leaves (1)
2 All kinds of leaves (2)

Photo Book reference Pages 4 and 5

QCA links
The children learn that green plants need light in order to grow well and that they make new plant material, using air and water in the presence of light. They learn that for this to take place, the plant needs leaves. (QCA Unit 6A)

Activities (continued)

● Ask the children what they know about the roots of plants. Ask; *What are they for?* Remind them of their previous learning about roots (they take in water and dissolved minerals from the soil, and help to anchor the plant). *What do they think happens to the water which plants take in? How does it escape from the plants and where does it go?*

● They could set up an investigation to find out if water escapes through the leaves of plants. Tie small plastic bags (or fasten them with elastic bands) over some of the leaves of a potted plant, such as a geranium, and observe what happens each day:

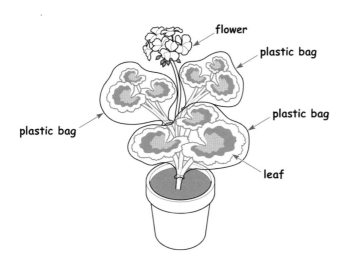

A geranium with small plastic bags over the leaves.

● *What can the children see on the inside of the bags?* If they say *condensation*, ask them what condensation is made of. Ask: *Where has this water come from?* Since the bags were tied over the leaves, and not the entire plant and its pot, the water cannot have come from the damp soil or potting compost. The children could explain what happens to the water taken in through the roots of plants, how it is used and where it goes afterwards, and relate this to what they know about the water cycle.

Higher-achieving children
Challenge them to find out how trees survive the winter without leaves.

Lower-achieving children
Provide a word bank to help them to describe the leaves of plants. When writing a report of their investigation to find out if water escapes from the leaves of plants, they could begin by drawing a flow chart on which they write what they know and what they observe, and make links between these.

Plenary session

◆ Draw out the importance of leaves in keeping a plant alive; they contain the green pigment which helps them to convert air, water and gases from the air into food.

Vocabulary

carbohydrate, cell, chlorophyll, compound leaf, condensation, leaflet, light, lobe, matt, serrated, simple leaf, variegated

3 An arum plant

QCA links
The children learn about the ways in which plants are suited to their habitats. (QCA Unit 6A)

Background information

The arum comes from the equatorial rain forests of Sumatra. The plant can reach a height of 6 metres. The largest recorded flower was 2.9 m tall, growing from an underground tuber 300 times the size of a potato. It is also known as the 'corpse flower' because the flower gives off a smell similar to rotting flesh – designed by nature to attract the carrion beetles and dung beetles which pollinate it. Its leaves are enormous – up to 5 metres across.

Starting points

- Ask the children if they think there is any reason for the shapes, colours, patterns and smells of plants. *Do they help the plant in any way?* Invite them to give examples.
- Remind them about what a plant needs in order to survive: water, sunlight, nutrients, air. Ask: *Do all plants need these in the same amounts?* Discuss what the children know about the differences between the needs of different plants.

Using the pictures

- ❑ Tell the children that this plant produces the largest flower in the world. *What can they find out from the photograph about its habitat?* Clues include the trees, leaves on the ground and the shade.
- ❑ Tell the children that this is an equatorial rain forest. Ask them what kind of conditions the plant has to adapt to.
- ❑ Ask them to describe all parts of the plant, and to make notes about how they think its structure helps it to survive in this place.
- ❑ Discuss the ways in which plants are pollinated, and tell them that the arum is pollinated by carrion beetles and dung beetles, which are attracted by its smell (similar to rotting flesh). Tell them that the plant is able to heat the flower, making the smell more intense, in order to attract these insects.

Activities

- ● Ask the children to use secondary sources, including the Internet (see **Resources**), to find out more about the arum plant and how it has adapted to its habitat. They could make notes, and then use their notes to help them to write a report. Encourage them to organise their notes under headings: for example, *Habitat conditions* (temperature, sunlight, rainfall, soil type), *Size*, *Reproduction*.

Higher-achieving children
Ask them to compare the arum plant with other tropical rainforest plants (see **Resources**). *What similarities and differences can they find between the ways in which the plants survive in these environments?*

Lower-achieving children
Encourage them to begin by looking at a familiar plant in the school grounds. Ask them how the arum plant is similar (it has a stem, leaves, roots and flower, it needs water, air and sunlight). Ask them how it is different (they could compare the colour, shape and size of the stem, leaves and flower). Ask them how the plants' habitats are similar and different. Draw out the ways in which some of the differences between the plants are related to their habitats.

Plenary session

- ◆ Draw out the ways in which the arum is suited to its environment, and why it would not survive in certain other environments: for example, a desert, grassland or a very cold place.

Vocabulary

arum, habitat, nutrient, pollinate, rain forest, tropical, tuber

Interdependence and adaptation

Photo Book reference Page 7

4 Fertilisers

QCA links

The children learn that fertilisers are often added to soils to provide plants with the nutrients they need. They turn scientific questions into a form which can be investigated, and draw conclusions from their investigations. (QCA Unit 6A)

Background information

Fertilisers add nutrients such as phosphates, nitrates, potassium and calcium to the soil to replace those used up by plants. In a natural environment, these nutrients are replaced by decomposing plant and animal material. Decomposition is aided by micro-organisms. Where land is used for crops or gardens, fertilisers are added to promote the growth of plants. A problem which can result is the build-up of nutrients in watercourses, and the subsequent increase of algae. Algae use sunlight to make food during daylight hours; this adds oxygen to the water; but they consume oxygen at night, leading to a low oxygen level in the morning. This can suffocate aquatic animals. Algae also block out sunlight, hampering the growth of plants in the water.

Starting points

■ Before the lesson, invite a gardener or farmer (or both) to list any substances he or she adds to the soil. Ask: *Are particular fertilisers used for certain plants?* (See Using the picture.)

■ Ask the children if they do any gardening, or know people who do. *Do they add anything to the soil (apart from water)?* Discuss why gardeners and farmers add materials to the soil. *What difference do they make?*

Using the picture

❏ Begin with the words on the label of 'Miracle Gro'. Ask: *What does this name suggest?* Ask the children to find out as much as they can from the photograph about the materials which gardeners add to the soil. *What are the materials called?*

❏ Ask: *Where does manure come from, and how can it improve soil? How is potting compost different from soil, and why do people use it instead of soil?*

❏ *Does it matter which fertilisers are used?* Discuss whether some plants might need different fertilisers, and why. The children should be able to read parts of the labels of the packages. Let them read what the gardeners and farmers said about the materials they add to the soil.

Activities

● Ask the children to plan an investigation to find out about the effects of different fertilisers on a plant. *How many plants should they test? How can they find out if some fertilisers are better than others for particular plants?* Different groups could work with different plants. Use seedlings, because seeds do not need fertiliser. Suitable plants include geranium, busy lizzie, sweet pea, tomato.

● Use *Photocopiable sheet 1* to plan a fair test to investigate the effects of a common fertiliser on a plant. They should ensure that the plants are provided with sufficient light, warmth and water, and that conditions are the same for both plants.

● In addition to measuring the plants they could photograph them, count the leaves and flowers and notice any changes in colour.

Consult school/LEA health and safety guidelines. Children should not touch fertilisers. Provide plastic gloves.

Higher-achieving children

They could find out if one fertiliser is better than another for a specific plant.

Lower-achieving children

Draw out the need to measure and record the heights of the plants at the start of the investigations in order to be able to compare the effects of fertilisers on growth.

Plenary session

◆ Ask: *Are fertilisers useful, or do gardeners waste their money when they buy them?* The children should use the results of their investigations to justify their answers. *How is feeding plants different from feeding animals?* Explain that animals have to eat in order to live, but that plants make their own food, with the help of nutrients from the soil.

Vocabulary

algae, chemicals, fertiliser, manure, nutrients

Interdependence and adaptation

Photo Book reference Page 8

5 Tree key

QCA links
The children learn to use keys to identify plants in local habitats. (QCA Unit 6A)

Background information

These common British trees are deciduous (they shed their leaves in the winter). Ash has a grooved, greyish bark, small pointed leaflets growing in pairs and clusters of yellowish white flowers with no petals, which produce hanging bunches of winged seeds. Hawthorn has serrated leaves with ridged veins, growing with alternately interspersed thorns, and small white flowers which produce red berries. Horse chestnut has large leaves with five or seven finely-toothed leaflets, with prominent veins, spreading like fingers, and white flowers, hanging in clusters, which produce chestnuts in hard, green, spiked shells. Its spreading canopy creates a large area of shade. English oak has medium-sized, wavy-edged leaves, growing in pairs or threes along the twigs, female flowers (tiny yellowish balls) and male flowers (also yellow) hanging in catkin formation. Rowan has serrated leaflets (slightly narrower than those of the ash) and small white flowers (similar to hawthorn) which produce clusters of red berries. Sycamore has greyish bark, large-lobed leaves with serrated edges and clusters of white flowers which produce pairs of winged seeds.

Starting point

■ *Can the children name a tree? What do they know about it?* They could describe its bark, flowers, leaves, seeds or trunk. Invite the others to add what they know. Build up descriptions of familiar trees. Ask: *Do they lose their leaves in winter or are they evergreens?* Introduce the word *deciduous*.

Using the pictures

❑ Review the children's previous learning about keys for classifying and identifying plants. Draw out that a key depends on questions which separate a group of plants into two, then separate those into two and so on until each plant has been separated from the others. Ask them what questions they could ask to separate a group of trees into two. Explain that the questions must be answerable by *Yes* or *No*.

❑ Ask them what questions the words in the diamond shapes on the key represent: for example, *Simple leaves* is a short way of writing *Does it have simple leaves?*

❑ *Do the children know what simple and compound leaves are?* Ask them to look at the ash, horse chestnut and rowan and they will see the leaflets which form the leaves.

Activities

● Mask the captions and ask the children to use the key to identify the trees.

● Provide other pictures of these trees from different sources, mask any captions and ask the children to use the key to identify them.

● They could make their own keys with additional trees: for example, beech, birch, cypress, fir, holly, larch, Scots pine, sitka spruce, willow, yew. Ask them to make a factfile about each tree: include pictures of the entire tree and close-ups of its bark, flowers, seeds and leaves. They could use computer software for devising keys.

Higher-achieving children
Encourage them to make as large a key as possible.

Lower-achieving children
Show them how to separate the factfile about the trees physically when they answer a question about them: for example, *Does it have berries?*

Plenary session

◆ Draw out that a key can be used to identify a plant by focusing on the differences between it and all other plants.

Vocabulary

acorn, alternate, ash, berry, canopy, catkin, compound leaf, deciduous, hawthorn, horse chestnut, key, leaflet, lobe, oak, rowan, simple leaf, sycamore

Interdependence and adaptation

6 Moss on lava on Surtsey

Photo Book reference Page 9

QCA links
The children learn about the different conditions in which plants live. They construct food chains for a particular habitat. (QCA Unit 6A)

Background information

Surtsey is a volcanic island, south-west of the Vestmannaeyjar (Westmen Islands) off the southern coast of Iceland, formed by an undersea volcanic eruption in 1963. By 1967, the island had developed an area of 2.5km² and elevations of up to 170m above sea level. The plant- and animal-life have been monitored since then. Bacteria and fungi became established very quickly; followed by mosses and then lichens. Plants and animals affect the developing habitat: plants such as moss begin to break down the lava to form soil; plants attract insects which, in turn, attract other animals. Plant and animal waste contribute to the developing soil, and the growth of plants with larger root systems helps to stabilise the soil. (See **Resources.**)

Starting points

- Review the children's previous learning about the needs of plants for growth. Ask: *Do they need soil? How do some plants grow where there is no soil?* Draw out that many of them have no roots, or have long roots which can creep around rocks.
- Ask them to locate Surtsey on a map and to say what they can find out about its physical features and climate.

Using the picture

- Ask the children what kind of environment this is. Focus on the most noticeable feature – the bare rock. Ask: *What is lava?* Explain that it is rock from a volcano, and tell them about the formation of Surtsey. Other features include an absence of trees or other plants, apart from moss. Discuss why this is. (There is no soil.) Ask: *What kind of conditions do plants on Surtsey face, apart from the lack of soil?* Draw out that the habitat is salty, due to the sea; the land is warmer than other land in the region; it is windswept and the air temperature is warm in the summer but very cold in the winter, with ice, frost and snow.
- Explain that moss can colonise a place without soil; it helps to break down the surface of the rock to form soil. Discuss where the moss and other plants on Surtsey came from and how they got there.

☐ *How is this environment similar to, and different from, the local environment or most other places the children know?* (It has no human features – only natural features.)

Activities

- Take the children to look for moss growing in the local environment. They could make notes about where it grows: the conditions of light, shade, dryness, dampness, shelter from the weather, exposure to weather. They could also use compasses to check the directions in which any moss-covered walls face.
- Ask the children to examine moss, using magnifying glasses. *What helps it to grow on walls (and on lava)?* Draw out that it has no roots.
- Review the children's previous learning about food chains. Ask them to find out about the animals and plants which have colonised Surtsey, and to construct some food chains. Explain that in a food chain the arrows point towards the consumer.

Higher-achieving children
They could find out which plants first colonised other volcanic areas of the world.

Lower-achieving children
Print out pictures which they can arrange to form food chains.

Plenary session

- Draw out that the seeds and spores of plants can be carried by the wind, water and animals, but that not all of them can survive in the places where they arrive. Explain that food chains usually begin with a plant (a producer).

Vocabulary

colonise, consumer, eruption, fungus, habitat, lava, lichen, moss, producer, soil, volcanic, volcano

Interdependence and adaptation

Photo Book reference Page 10

7 The Arizona Desert

QCA links
The children learn about the different conditions in which plants live, and about how they are suited to their habitats. (QCA Unit 6A)

Background information

Deserts are places with an annual precipitation of less than 250mm. The Arizona Desert has an average temperature of 20°C in winter and 39°C in summer. The organ pipe cactus has no leaves. This reduces water loss through transpiration. It stores water in its stems, has spines for shade and protection from animals and a waxy coating to seal in moisture. Many desert trees and shrubs, such as the Joshua tree and creosote bush, have small, spiny leaves or thorns to reduce transpiration and grow very long roots to reach moisture deep underground. The creosote bush has a taste and smell which animals dislike. The stomata (pores) on its leaves close in the day to retain water and open at night to absorb it. The ocotillo survives by lying dormant during dry periods. The waxy coating on the stems seals in moisture. After rain the octillo bursts into life, quickly growing new leaves to photosynthesise food and blooming within a few weeks. As soon as the seeds fall the leaves die and the plant becomes dormant again. This can happen five times a year.

Starting point

- Review the children's previous learning about what plants need in order to grow. *Can they grow in places which have very little water?* Ask them to name plants they know which need little water. Discuss the water needs of different potted plants.

Using the pictures

- Ask the children what kind of environment this is. *Is it hot or cold? How can they tell?* Ask them how the ripples on the sand might have been formed. They resemble ripples formed by water on a beach but were, in fact, formed by wind.
- *Can the children name this type of environment?* Ask them what they know about deserts. Ask: *Does it ever rain there? Is the weather always hot?* The children could find out.
- Ask: *How is this environment similar to, and different from, their local environment or most other places they know?* (It has no buildings or other human features – only natural features.) *Why does no one live there?*

Activities

- The children could find out about the ways in which desert plants survive. Encourage them to find out as much as possible from the photographs: for example, how thick, sap-filled stems, spines, thorns, tiny leaves, waxy coatings, woody stems and long roots might help.
- Remind them of their previous learning about the ways in which plants give off water (topics 1 and 2). They could examine the leaves of plants through a microscope and make labelled drawings of what they see. Draw attention to the tiny holes in the surface of a leaf which let water and gases escape. Tell the children about the plants which can close these holes during the day to retain water.

Higher-achieving children
They could plan an investigation to find out about the effects of very bright, hot light on the leaves of a plant: compare a plant with large leaves with one that has needle-like leaves. If a greenhouse is not available, put the plants in a glass or Perspex frame.

Lower-achieving children
Help them to read the labels (including symbols) of plants from garden centres or shops, and find out about their needs for light or shade and for water. Ask: *Which plant would have the best chance of surviving in a desert?*

Plenary session

- Draw out that plants grow in places which are suited to their structures, behaviour and life cycles, and that over many years they adapt to their environments.

Vocabulary

Arizona, cactus, creosote bush, desert, dormant, Joshua tree, ocotillo, organ pipe cactus, transpiration

Interdependence and adaptation

Photo Book reference Page 11

8 Alaska

The children learn about the different conditions in which plants live, and about how they are suited to their habitats.
(QCA Unit 6A)

Background information

The Alaskan tundra has an average winter temperature of –34°C and an annual rainfall of about 250mm. Summer temperatures average 10C°, with permanent sunlight for two months. Saxifrage survives in poor soil, cold climates and high altitudes. It has an underground root system for storing carbohydrates during cold weather. Hairs on its leaves protect it from cold. The Arctic poppy bursts into life while the weather is warm, produces flowers and seeds and then dies in the winter. The seeds germinate once the weather becomes warm. Its flowers turn, like satellite dishes, to catch the sun's rays during long, cool summer days. Lichens are fungi combined with algae, in a symbiotic relationship (each contributes to the other). They have no roots and so do not obtain nutrients from the soil. Algae produce food from the sun's energy. Lichens are very sensitive to air pollution.

Starting point

■ Review the children's previous learning about what plants need for growth. Ask: *Can plants grow without warmth?* Invite the children to discuss their ideas. *Do they think plants can germinate without warmth?*

Using the pictures

❑ Mask the captions and ask the children what kind of environment is shown in the centre and top-right photographs. Focus on features such as the snow and absence of trees. *Is it hot or cold? How can they tell?* They might think the top-right picture shows a desert because of its barrenness and because the ground might appear to be covered with sand (this is, in fact, mosses and other low-growing plants).

❑ *Can the children name this type of environment? What do they know about Arctic environments? Do they ever have sunshine? Is it always cold?* Point out that the Tundra rainfall is similar to that of deserts, but it is much colder. Unmask the captions and ask them if they know where Alaska is. They could locate it on a map.

Activities

● The children could find out about the ways in which Arctic plants survive. Encourage them to find out as much as possible from the photographs: for example, how a lack of leaves or stems, tiny leaves and long roots might help. Remind them of their previous learning about the ways in which plants behave in the winter: for example, some die in the autumn after producing seeds from which new plants will grow, but others only appear to die, merely shedding their leaves and becoming dormant until the spring.

● They could plan an investigation to find out about the effects of extreme cold on different plants: for example, plants known to survive in cold climates, such as alpines, heathers and saxifrage, and plants known to prefer warm climates, such as busy lizzies, cacti and geraniums.

Higher-achieving children
They could use the Internet (see **Resources**) to find out about other plants which grow in Arctic environments and make notes about the ways in which each plant survives the extremely low winter temperatures.

Lower-achieving children
Help them to read the labels (including symbols) of plants from garden centres or shops and find out about their needs for warmth and how frost affects them. *Which would have the best chance of surviving in Alaska?*

Plenary session

◆ Draw out that plants grow in places which are suited to their structures, behaviour and life cycles, and that over many years they adapt to their habitats.

Vocabulary

Alaska, algae, Arctic Circle, Arctic poppy, climate, dormant, dwarf willow, lichen, saxifrage, Tundra

Micro-organisms

Photo Book reference Page 12

9 Influenza vírus

QCA links

The children learn that there are very small organisms called micro-organisms which are too small to be seen without a powerful microscope and can be harmful. They learn about the reasons for some common illnesses. (QCA Unit 6B)

Background information

Influenza ('flu) is caused by a virus which is constantly mutating, leading to new strains. Immunity against one strain (from exposure or immunisation) does not protect against others. Symptoms are similar to those of the common cold (but without a runny nose), accompanied by severe headache, cough and, as a result of the fever, intermittent sweating and shivering and severe aches and pains. The worst symptoms usually last for three to five days. The usual treatment is to stay indoors, drink plenty of fluids, relieve fever symptoms with paracetamol, aspirin (not for children under 16), ibuprofen or other anti-inflammatory drugs and relieve respiratory symptoms with decongestants, cough medicines, gargles or lozenges.

Starting point

■ Ask the children about any recent illnesses they have had. *What symptoms did they have and what treatment were they given?* Ask them if they know how they became ill, and discuss what is meant by a germ, micro-organism or virus. Tell them that illnesses can be caused when different types of micro-organisms (which are often called germs) get into their bodies, and that these micro-organisms can get into the body in different ways.

Using the picture

❑ Ask the children which illness is caused by this virus. Tell them that the virus cannot be seen without a very powerful microscope; it measures only 200 nanometres (1 nanometre = one ten-millionth of a centimetre).

❑ Ask them which parts of the body are affected by influenza. *How do they think the virus enters the body and gets to those parts?* Explain that we breathe it in.

❑ Discuss the times when people are at risk from influenza, and why older people are offered vaccinations against the disease. Ask: *Why are people more vulnerable in the winter?*

Activities

● The children could consider what they have learned about influenza and suggest ways in which people can protect themselves against it (in addition to vaccination).

● They could make notes from information leaflets and the Internet about influenza and the steps people can take to protect themselves from it. Ask them to design a display, website or poster to advise others about influenza. Different groups could take responsibility for different aspects: the virus, how we catch influenza, its effects, prevention, treatment and so on.

Higher-achieving children

They could find out about large influenza epidemics: for example, numbers of sufferers, how the epidemic affected doctors and hospitals and its effects on industry.

Lower-achieving children

To help them to appreciate the size of the virus, ask them to draw a line one millimetre long. Explain that a million viruses could fit along the line. Encourage them to use this understanding to explain why influenza is easily spread by one person to another.

Plenary session

◆ Draw out that a virus is a microscopic living organism which can enter our bodies and make us ill.

Vocabulary

cold, fever, 'flu, germ, infection, influenza, micro-organism, symptom, virus

Micro-organisms

10 Mouldy food

Photo Book reference Page 13

QCA links
The children learn that micro-organisms can cause food to decay. They make suggestions about observing food, bearing in mind the need for safety, and learn that food needs to be handled and stored with care. (QCA Unit 6B)

Background information

Many moulds can be seen with the naked eye but the micro-organisms which cause them cannot. Moulds are fungi composed of many cells. Most of them have a thread-like structure, live on plant or animal material and thrive in warm, humid conditions. Under a microscope they look like narrow mushrooms, with root threads which can extend very deeply into the food, and a stalk rising above the food. They reproduce through spores (formed at the end of the stalk), which give mould its colour and can be transported by air, water or insects.

Starting points

- Ask the children how food is stored at home: for example, in a fridge or freezer, in sealed boxes or bags. Discuss why different foods are stored in different ways – why some need to be stored in a fridge but others do not, and why some need to be stored in a freezer. Ask: *Why should packets, boxes, jars, tins and bottles be sealed?*
- Discuss why some foods keep better if they are not sealed in boxes or bags, or put in a fridge or freezer.

Using the picture

- Ask the children what has happened to this strawberry. If they say it is mouldy, ask them to describe the mould: its colour and texture, how it affects the strawberry and how it is attached to the fruit. *Do they know what a mould is?* Introduce the term *fungus,* if necessary, and ask them about other fungi they have seen: for example, mushrooms and toadstools (there is no scientific difference between a mushroom and a toadstool, but *toadstool* is usually used only for poisonous mushrooms).
- Discuss what makes food mouldy. Ask: *Where does the mould come from? Does it come from the strawberry? If not, where else could it come from?* Draw out that mould is a living organism. Its spread can be compared with seed dispersal in plants, but it reproduces through spores, rather than seeds, because it is not a flowering plant.

Activities

- Ask the children what can be done to stop food going mouldy. In groups, they could list their ideas.
- Invite feedback: for example, cover the food, put it in a fridge or freezer. *Why?* Discuss why some foods do not go mouldy quickly at room temperature: for example, cereals, dried fruit, dried beans. Ask: *Why do dried fruits stay mould-free for longer than fresh fruits? What is the difference between them?*

 As soon as mould develops on food it should be wrapped up and disposed of. Do not let the children handle it.

- Ask the children to use **Photocopiable sheet 2** to plan an investigation into the effects of different storage conditions on the growth of mould on a piece of bread. They could work in pairs, each pair investigating different conditions and sharing their results. Ensure that they understand that mould spores can land on food from the air, and that mould is a living organism. Ask them about the combination of conditions provided: dry, humid, warm, cold, freezing.

Higher-achieving children
They could also compare how well fresh and dried foods stay mould-free: for example, plums and prunes, grapes and raisins, fresh and dried apricots.

Lower-achieving children
Discuss what condition is being changed in their investigation: temperature, light, dryness/humidity, whether or not the food is covered.

Plenary session

- Draw out that moulds are living organisms which need warmth and humidity (but not light) in order to grow.

Vocabulary

fungi, fungus, germ, humid, micro-organism, mould, mushroom, spore, toadstool

Micro-organisms

Photo Book reference Page 14

11 Louis Pasteur

QCA links
The children learn that micro-organisms feed and grow and that they can be used to prevent the diseases they cause. (QCA Unit 6B)

Background information

Vaccination is the use of a very weak strain of a disease to encourage the body to produce antibodies, in order to destroy the microbes which cause the disease. The antibodies give protection against future exposure to the disease.

Starting points

■ Ask the children what they know about micro-organisms. *How do they affect food?*

■ Ask them about vaccinations they have had. *Do they know why they had them?* Ask them how we catch diseases (see topic 10) and discuss how the body responds to infections. Explain how vaccination can protect us from diseases by encouraging the body to produce antibodies.

Using the picture

❏ Ask the children to read the passage with a partner, and to list the words or phrases which refer to micro-organisms or their effects. Invite feedback.

❏ They could make notes about how Louis Pasteur killed microbes in the broth which he made. Ask: *What can we learn from this about killing germs in food?* Discuss why the broth is still mould-free today and what this tells us about preserving food.

❏ Discuss why other scientists thought that living things came from the food. (Probably, they did not think they could have come from anywhere else.) *How was Pasteur's theory different?*

❏ Draw out how Pasteur used what he had learned from his work on microbes in beer to help him in his work on vaccines. Also draw out how he made his test on the anthrax vaccine fair.

Activities

● Ask the children to use secondary sources (such as books, leaflets, CDs or the Internet) to find out about diseases for which vaccines have been created (including the dates and the scientists involved). They could write a report.

● *Photocopiable sheet 3* provides a planning sheet to help the children to prepare a report about vaccines for diseases.

Higher-achieving children

In mixed-ability groups, they could take responsibility for organising the script for a television report and for matching it to the images, dialogue or action on the screen.

Lower-achieving children

Help them to write a caption or headline for an image to be used in their report. Encourage them to read it aloud and to use it as the basis for part of the script.

Plenary session

◆ Draw out that our bodies create materials called antibodies to destroy the microbes which cause a disease, and that these give long-term (sometimes lifelong) protection from the disease.

Vocabulary

antibody, control group, disease, ferment, germ, microbe, micro-organism, vaccination

Micro-organisms

12 Useful micro-organisms

Photo Book reference Page 15

QCA links
The children learn that micro-organisms feed and grow and can be useful in food production. They make careful observations and draw conclusions from them. (QCA Unit 6B)

Background information

Micro-organisms are used in yogurt, cheese, tea, beer and wine production. The bacteria which change the consistency and taste of milk to form yogurt are usually known as a *culture*. 'Live' yogurt contains living bacteria but yogurt which is not 'live' has been heated, killing the bacteria after they have altered the milk.

Starting point

■ Re-read the first paragraph of topic 11 (Louis Pasteur) and focus on the word 'fermented'. *Do the children know what it means?* They could look it up. *What does this tell them about the use of microbes in beer?* Draw out that some microbes are useful: for example, those which ferment beer, wine and tea, but that others are harmful: for example, those which turn beer sour or cause mould on foods or make people ill. *Do the children know of any other foods in which microbes are useful?*

Using the pictures

❑ Ask the children which of the foods in the pictures they think are produced using microbes. (All of them.) Discuss what happens to milk which has been kept for a long time. Micro-organisms break down the lactose in lactic acid, causing casein (the main protein in milk) to form insoluble lumps. Cheese is made by solidifying milk protein, but this cannot be allowed to happen naturally because there could also be harmful bacteria. The milk is pasteurised (heated to a high temperature for several minutes) to kill the harmful bacteria and then rennet, which contains useful bacteria, is added. During the curing process some bacteria produce carbon dioxide, forming bubbles which leave holes in the cheese.

❑ *Do the children know where tea comes from, or even that it is made from leaves?* Explain that the flavour develops while the leaves (still moist) are left in a warm place to ferment (bacteria change their flavour). Different teas are produced by stopping the fermentation process at different stages.

Activities

● The children could make yogurt. A simple method is to mix equal amounts of boiling milk and cold milk, and then stir in a tablespoonful of live natural yogurt. Pour the mixture into a sterilised wide-mouthed flask and leave it for 24 hours.

Keep the children away from boiling milk. Once the hot and cold milk have been mixed the children can take part in yogurt-making. Ensure that they wash their hands and all equipment is sterilised.

● To find out about the importance of live organisms in yogurt-making, the children could also try replacing the live yogurt with ordinary natural yogurt and comparing the results. Also try adding live yogurt to boiling milk and leaving it for 24 hours in a flask. Let the children examine the product. Ask the children what they have learned about the effects of temperature on bacteria.

● They could experiment with flavouring the yogurt, using chopped fruit and honey, and write a recipe for a flavoured yogurt.

Higher-achieving children
Ask them if they think the live culture would convert the milk to yogurt if it were placed in a refrigerator. Let them carry out a fair test to find out.

Lower-achieving children
Provide headings to help them to write a recipe: for example, *Equipment, Ingredients, Method*.

Plenary session

◆ Explain that micro-organisms are killed by high temperatures, but that some of them are useful.

Vocabulary

bacteria, bacterium, carbon dioxide, culture, ferment, microbe, micro-organism, pasteurise, protein

Micro-organisms

Photo Book reference Page 16

13 Yeast

Background information

Yeast is a fungus which needs food, moisture and warmth in order to grow and reproduce. In the investigation, the mixture containing sugar and warm water increases in size more than the others and becomes bubbly; the balloon inflates slightly because of the gases produced (mainly carbon dioxide). In warm conditions the fungus grows and reproduces, especially if it is mixed with sugar or starch (on which it feeds), but high temperatures kill it. Fresh yeast can be frozen or refrigerated; these processes do not kill it but render it dormant. Dried yeast is dormant because of the lack of water.

Starting points

- Review the children's previous learning about micro-organisms (topics 10−12). Ask: *In what ways do micro-organisms change foods? What types of helpful micro-organism act on foods such as yogurt and cheese?* (Bacteria.) *How are harmful bacteria removed from food?* Discuss the importance of sterile equipment and the use of high temperatures in killing micro-organisms.
- Ask the children to name foods which stay mould-free at room temperature. Explain that moist food in cans, bottles, jars or packets is usually heated to a high temperature before it is put in sterile containers with airtight seals. Once a container is opened the food will not stay fresh for long.
- Do the children know why dried foods, such as raisins, pasta and rice stay fresh? Would they stay fresh if they were not kept dry?

Using the pictures

- ❑ Ask the children what they can find out about fresh yeast from the picture. (It is a solid material with a creamy white colour, it can be dried to form small granules and it is a living organism.)
- ❑ *How do they think yeast manufacturers produce yeast?* Draw out the needs of living organisms (food and water) and explain that yeast can be grown from a single cell (point out the cells in the photograph and explain that all parts of all living things are made up of cells).

QCA links

The children learn that micro-organisms feed and grow and can be useful in food production. They make suggestions about what yeast needs in order to feed and grow, make and compare careful observations and draw conclusions about the effect of yeast on dough. (QCA Unit 6B)

The cell is put into a test tube with a moist, sugary food (a type of molasses), kept warm but not too hot and allowed to grow into a thick, creamy, frothy material. It is moved into a large container, where it continues to grow. The solids are separated from the liquid and the mixture is washed. It is kept cold to prevent further growth and reproduction.

Activities

- Provide powdered yeast and, if possible, fresh yeast and ask the children whether they think each is dead or able to grow. *What could they do to it to find out?* ***Photocopiable sheet 4*** suggests some ideas for testing yeast to find out what conditions the micro-organisms need in order to grow. They could also find out what temporarily stops their growth and what kills them, by heating yeast in an oven, or putting it in a fridge or freezer overnight, and then repeating the investigation.

Higher-achieving children
They could plan an investigation to find out about other materials on which yeast can feed, and to compare its growth when it feeds on different materials.

Lower-achieving children
Ensure that they understand what makes the bubbles in a yeast mixture and why the balloon placed over the end of the test tube inflates.

Plenary session

- ◆ Draw out that yeast produces gases when it feeds on starchy or sugary materials, and that these gases make bubbles in the material.

Vocabulary

carbon dioxide, fungi, fungus, gases, micro-organism, moisture, yeast

Micro-organisms

Photo Book reference Page 17

14 Alexander Fleming

QCA links
The children learn about an important scientific discovery connected with mould. (QCA Unit 6B)

Background information

Penicillin is a fungus. Fungi have been used in medicine for thousands of years without people realising what they were. More than three thousand years ago a Chinese remedy for boils and other skin infections used mouldy soybean curd. Another ancient remedy involved the use of warm earth to treat infected injuries. Although the development of the mould on Alexander Fleming's petri dish was an accident, the discovery of penicillin arose because his earlier work prepared him for it.

Starting points

- Review the children's previous learning about micro-organisms (topics 10-12). Ask them what they know about moulds. Draw out that they are living organisms which scientists place in a different class from plants or animals. They have some similarities with plants (they are alive and need water) but have neither leaves nor flowers and cannot produce their own food. They reproduce by means of airborne spores, rather than seeds. *Do the children know another word for this type of organism?* (Fungus)
- Ask for examples of fungi (yeast, mushrooms, toadstools). You could also mention that fungi can grow on human skin: for example, the one which causes athlete's foot. Discuss the conditions in which this fungus grows (damp and warm).

Using the pictures

- ❑ Remind the children that some fungi can be useful, and tell them that they are going to find out about one which is used in medicine.
- ❑ Ask them to read the passage about Alexander Fleming. *In what ways had the work of Louis Pasteur prepared the way for the discovery of penicillin?* Explain that bacteria were first observed in 1683 by Antony van Leeuwenhoek, the inventor of the microscope. Draw out that Pasteur knew that tiny organisms existed and so he looked for them in the beer he was testing. Fleming was able to build on this knowledge; he was looking for a chemical to destroy the harmful bacteria which cause infections in wounds, without harming the patient.

Activities

- The children could use magnifying glasses or microscopes to examine different types of non-poisonous mushrooms. They could make observational drawings. *Can they identify the spores?* They could make spore prints by leaving a mature mushroom (not a button mushroom) overnight on a piece of Perspex with a cup over it. Because the spores fall straight downwards, it should leave a spore print showing the pattern of the mushroom's gills. The colour of the spore print helps in identifying mushrooms from field guides (see **Resources**).
- *Photocopiable sheet 5* provides some questions about the pictures and the passage. Ask the children to look at the pictures and read the captions and the passage to find the answers to the questions which will help them to complete the puzzle on this sheet.

Higher-achieving children
They could compile an information book about edible mushrooms. Ask them to plan for one page per mushroom, including a picture with a caption and a spore print, and to decide what headings to include: for example, height, diameter, colour, habitat, any similar-looking mushrooms, warnings (about similarities with poisonous varieties).

Lower-achieving children
An adult could read the passage with the children before the lesson and highlight new vocabulary.

Plenary session

- ◆ Draw out that penicillin is an antibiotic made from a mould (fungus) and that mushrooms belong to the same group of living organisms.

Vocabulary

antibiotic, fungi, fungus, gases, infection, mould, penicillin, petri dish

Micro-organisms

15 Treating sewage

Background information

A septic tank is used for treating sewage and waste water from properties not linked to a mains sewerage system. Waste water, including solid matter, enters a chamber in the tank where some solid material settles at the bottom and then passes into another chamber, where microbes digest it. Floating solid particles are filtered out before they, too, are treated by microbes. The water which emerges from the tanks is clear and contains no harmful material. It is released into the ground. The type of reed bed shown here is an artificial wetland planted with specially selected species of reed which absorb oxygen from the air and release it through their roots. This creates a perfect habitat for micro-organisms which break down soluble material in sewage.

Starting point

■ Ask the children what they remember from geography lessons about the water which enters their homes, the school or other buildings. Ask: *Where does it come from? How is it brought into the buildings? Where does waste water and sewage go?* Discuss where the pipes take this waste water (containing some solid material). *Where does it end up?* Explain that pipes dump sewage into the sea in some places, but that it has to be treated first. Also, point out that some buildings are not connected to sewers because they are too far away from them. *What do the children think happens to waste water and sewage from these buildings?* If the school is in a rural area the children might know the answer to this. If not, encourage them to consider the possibilities.

Using the pictures

❑ Ask the children to look at the first picture and to read the caption. *Do they know what a septic tank is?* Ask them to look for clues elsewhere on the page. Remind them of the discussion about what might happen when buildings are not connected to the main sewers. Ask them how a tank like this could help. Explain that at one time tanks which collected sewage had to be emptied using pumps; the material was taken away in trucks and the water filtered into the ground; but,

QCA links

The children learn that micro-organisms are living organisms which can bring about decay, which can be beneficial. This activity links with work on Unit 6C (More about dissolving); it provides an opportunity for the children to review their previous work on separating insoluble materials by sieving and filtering. (QCA Units 6B and 6C)

nowadays, septic tanks are designed to treat the waste material. Ask: *What could be added to the material in the tank to change it?* Remind the children about useful micro-organisms and explain that there are microbes which can digest material from sewage and break down solid material into small pieces. They change the material, making it harmless.

❑ *Can the children think of ways in which a reed bed can treat sewage?* Remind them of the role of microbes, and about their previous learning about habitats.

Activities

● If possible, take the children to see a sewage treatment plant or reed bed; or ask a representative from a septic tank manufacturer or reed bed producer to come and talk to them. Before the visit, help the children to prepare questions which will help them to find out what they want to know.

Higher-achieving children
Encourage them to find out in greater detail about the processes involved in using microbes to treat sewage.

Lower-achieving children
Before the activity, take them around the school to identify the pipes which bring clean water to the school and take waste water away (including run-off from roofs and playground surfaces). They could mark these on a prepared map of the school and make a key for their maps.

Plenary session

◆ Draw out that micro-organisms can change materials in ways which help us.

Vocabulary

filter, liquid, mesh, microbe, micro-organism, reed bed, separate, septic tank, sewage, solid

More about dissolving

Photo Book reference Page 19

16 Riddles

QCA links
The children review their previous learning that insoluble materials can be separated by sieving. They make careful measurements. (QCA Unit 6C)

Background information

The photograph shows children at Killhope lead mine in County Durham. They are trying out the riddles which were once used for separating larger pieces of rock from smaller pieces among the discarded rock dug out of the mine. The mine-owners tried to collect every scrap of lead – none was wasted. The riddles are attached to a mechanism which shakes them, to make the smaller pieces fall through the riddle. The larger fragments, which do not fit through the holes, settle on top of the riddle, with the largest fragments settling on top of the rest.

Starting point

■ Ask volunteers to describe a sieve and to give instructions for using it for a purpose of their choice. Encourage them to think of as many different types of sieve as they can, and as many different uses as possible: for example, vegetable strainers, tea strainers, the wire baskets in chip pans, fishing nets. Ask: *What similarities are there between all sieves?* (They all have holes, which allow some materials to pass through them but not others.) *What are the differences between the sieves they have described?* (They are of different sizes, have holes of different sizes and are made of different materials.) Discuss what makes each sieve suitable for its purpose.

Using the picture

❑ Introduce the word *riddle* for sieve and ask the children about the types of sieve which are known as riddles: for example, those used in gardening for separating soil particles of different sizes or for separating stones from soil.

❑ Ask them how the riddle in the picture is being used. Tell them that it is part of the equipment of an old lead mine. Discuss what is being separated from what, and how. Draw out that the riddle cannot help the users to distinguish between lead and other stones, but that it makes this task easier by separating out all the larger pieces.

❑ *What could be done to separate out the larger pieces among those which fall through the riddle, and so help the workers to find the pieces of lead among them?*

Activities

● Give the children a mixed collection of coins and ask them to work in groups to design a series of riddles for sorting money into sets of coins of the same value. Once they have agreed on what to do, they could split the work so that different children (individuals or pairs) work on riddles of different sizes. Encourage them to use rulers to make careful measurements.

● Discuss their plans and encourage them to make their machines from materials which are easy to work with: for example, card, paper and lightweight strips of wood.

Higher-achieving children
They could make a device which is activated only by coins of a certain denomination: for example, when a 5p coin lands in a container, it could operate a see-saw type of mechanism.

Lower-achieving children
They could design and make a device which separates pennies from £1 coins.

Plenary session

◆ Draw out that a riddle, or sieve, separates pieces of solid materials of different sizes or separates solid particles from water. Materials can pass through a riddle, or sieve, if they are smaller than the holes in it.

Vocabulary

dissolved, mesh, riddle, separate, sieve

More about dissolving

Photo Book reference Page 20

17 Drinking water

QCA links
The children learn that solids which do not dissolve in water can be separated by filtering. They describe a scientific process in a series of sequential steps. (QCA Unit 6C)

Background information

Space does not permit a complete description and explanation of the processes involved in purifying water before it is supplied to consumers, but the main processes are: removing large pieces of solid material (using a grid); removing smaller pieces using a strainer; aerating; using chemicals to coagulate any remaining solid material; collecting this as sludge; filtering through carbon and killing bacteria with materials such as ozone and chlorine. More information can be found from your local water supplier (see **Resources**).

Starting point

■ If possible, take the children to a water treatment plant. Discuss why we cannot drink water from streams, lakes and rivers, even if it looks clean. Draw out that water which looks clean could have harmful materials dissolved in it: for example, pesticides and fertilisers, and animal waste. It could also contain harmful bacteria.

Using the picture

❑ Invite the children to take turns to describe a stage of the process of purifying water and transporting it to our homes. Discuss why strainers and chemicals are used.

❑ Ask them if they have heard of chlorine and if they know what it is. Explain that it is a gas, which can be mixed with other materials to form chemicals which kill bacteria. The children might be familiar with the use of chlorine to kill bacteria in swimming pools.

❑ Help them to make connections between the diagram and what they have seen at a water treatment plant.

Activities

● Show the children a jar of muddy water, containing other material such as small leaves and bits of wood, and ask them to think of ways of cleaning it. Ask:*What do we mean by cleaning?* Remind them of the first stage of the water treatment process. *What could they use to remove solid material from the water, and how can they do this?*

● Once the larger solid pieces have been removed ask them to work with a partner to plan a method of removing the mud. *Would a sieve work? What would be better?* Ask them to think about how they could set up the equipment, including a method of collecting the clean water. The following method could be used:

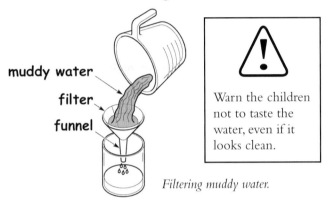

muddy water
filter
funnel

Warn the children not to taste the water, even if it looks clean.

Filtering muddy water.

● The children should write a report, including a diagram, to describe what they did and their results. Let them use a magnifying glass or microscope to look at filter paper so that they can see the tiny gaps between its fibres. *Can they explain why water passes through it but particles of mud do not?*

Higher-achieving children
Ask them to set up their water-cleaning system without help and to explain how it works.

Lower-achieving children
Show them the materials they could use in their water-purifying system. Ask them what will pass through the filter paper and what will not. Discuss why.

Plenary session

◆ Draw out that filter paper works in the same way as a riddle or sieve (see topic 16).

Vocabulary

bacteria, chemical, chlorine, clean, dissolve, filter, pump, purify, riddle, sieve

More about dissolving

Photo Book reference Page 21

18 Water mixtures

QCA links
The children turn ideas about what makes solids dissolve more quickly into a form which can be investigated. They decide how to carry out a fair test and what apparatus to use, make careful observations and measurements, make comparisons and draw conclusions. (QCA Unit 6C)

Background information

Tea leaves are insoluble in water but substances from them dissolve (they colour the water brown). Milk consists mainly of water with some materials dissolved and others suspended in it (they do not dissolve and do not sink to the bottom and any fat floats on top of the water.) Sugar and coffee dissolve in water. The molecules of a substance are held together by bonds. When materials dissolve these bonds are broken and the molecules are separated from one another. Heat and stirring help to break the bonds. The materials (solutes) mix with water (solvent) to form a solution and, where no new material is formed, they can be separated from the water by evaporation.

Starting point

■ Ask the children what is meant by *dissolve*. If they link it with melting, remind them about their previous learning about melting: for example, butter, ice and ice cream melt when they are warm without anything being added to them; dissolving is mixing with a liquid, such as water. *Do they remember the word for water, or any other liquid, with material dissolved in it?* (Solution.)

Using the picture

❑ Ask the children which materials in the photograph dissolve in water, and how they know. *How do they know that something from tea dissolves in water and that tea leaves, themselves, do not?* If they say that 'colour' dissolves in the water, point out that there is no such material as colour and that it must be a coloured *material*. Introduce the words *soluble* and *insoluble*.

❑ Ask the children to give an oral recount of making a cup of coffee or tea. Ask: *Why do we use hot water? Why do we stir the drink?*

Activities

● Ask the children what they can do to make sugar dissolve quickly. Remind them that if they change more than one thing at a time they will not know what made the difference.

● *Photocopiable sheet 6* will help them to plan what to do and to record the results.

● Different groups of children could try different ideas for making sugar dissolve quickly: for example, stirring or using warm water. Ask them how they will be able to compare. *What can they measure or observe?* They could try using a timer. Encourage them to repeat their investigations to check the results. They will need a 'control' against which to compare.

Higher-achieving children
They could investigate different types of sugar (including 'quick-dissolving' sugar) to find out which dissolves the most quickly. They could first make observations of the sizes of the granules of sugar. Ask them to create a graph on which to record their findings. They could draw the graph by hand or use graphing software. Ask: *Does sugar with small granules dissolve more quickly than sugar with large granules?*

Lower-achieving children
Help them to plan an investigation to find out if sugar always dissolves more quickly if it is stirred and if faster stirring makes any difference. Ask them what they must keep the same (the type of sugar, the temperature of the water and the amount of water and sugar).

Plenary session

◆ Ask the children to report and explain their results. Draw out that warm water and stirring speed up the process of dissolving.

Vocabulary

dissolve, evaporate, evaporation, heat, insoluble, maximum, stir, saturated, soluble, solute, solution, solvent

More about dissolving

19 Salt from the sea

QCA links
The children learn that when solids dissolve a clear solution is formed and that the solid cannot be separated by filtering, but can be separated by evaporating the water. (QCA Unit 6C)

Background information

Dissolved materials can be separated from water by evaporation as long as no new material has been formed. The sea is salty because rivers carry sediment containing salt into it. There is not enough salt in rivers to be noticeable. The sea receives water from millions of rivers. Water evaporates from the sea, leaving salts. Oceans and seas have had about the same salt content for millions of years. It has reached a steady state; dissolved salts are deposited on the seabed, to form new minerals, as fast as new salts are being added to the sea.

Starting point

■ Ask the children what they know about salt. *Is it a solid or a liquid? Is it soluble or insoluble in water?* Ask them how they can tell if there is salt in water. If they suggest tasting it, ask them how water which is not clean enough to taste can be tested for salt. Make a note of their ideas for use after discussing the picture.

Using the picture

❏ Ask the children how this salt could have been collected from the sea. *Could nets or filters have been used?* Ask them to explain their answers. Discuss how they could carry out an investigation involving tasting to find out if salt can be separated from water using a net, sieve or filter. Let them try pouring salty water through a sieve and a coffee filter. Also, try pouring undissolved salt through a sieve then a coffee filter. Ask: *How does salt change when it dissolves in water?*

❏ Return to the photograph. *How is this salt different from table salt?* The children should notice its brownish colour and that the granules are much bigger than table salt. Ask: *Could the granules pass through a filter? Could they pass through when dissolved in water?*

❏ Draw out that pieces of solid material become so tiny when dissolved that they can pass through the gaps in a filter. *Can we see the gaps? How do we know there are gaps?* (Water passes through filter paper.) The children could look at a coffee filter through a microscope or magnifying glass to see the tiny gaps between the fibres.

Activities

● The children could find out what makes the sea salty.

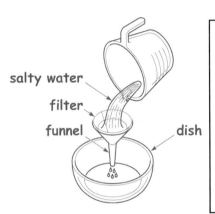

Ensure that all equipment is hygienic, so that the children can taste the water by dipping a cotton bud into it.

Putting salt into a filter.

● Pour 50ml of salty water into the filter. Ask the children to taste the water in the dish. *Is it salty?* Leave the water to evaporate, and ask the children what remains. (Salt). Repeat this, each day, for three or four days. Each time salty water is poured through the filter, salt is added to the dish. Salt dissolves in water, so it passes through the filter. More and more salt collects in the dish.

Higher-achieving children
They could test a collection of samples of non-drinking water to find out if anything is dissolved in them: for example, seawater, river water, tap water, bottled water.

Lower-achieving children
Ensure that they know the difference between dissolving and melting by showing examples of melting.

Plenary session

◆ Ask the children to use the results of their investigations to explain why the sea is salty.

Vocabulary

crystal, dissolve, evaporate, evaporation, liquid, separate, solid, soluble, solution

More about dissolving

20 A solar still

QCA links
The children make predictions about what happens when water from a solution evaporates and then test these predictions. (QCA Unit 6C)

Background information

Water can be separated from dissolved materials by evaporation and condensation, as long as no new material has been formed. Drinking water can be collected in this way from seawater and other non-drinking water. When water evaporates the unwanted materials in it are left behind.

Starting point

■ Ask the children what they have learned about seawater. *Can we drink it? Why not? Can we drink river or stream water?* Discuss how water from rivers and streams has to be treated to make it safe to drink (see topic 17).

Using the picture

❑ Remind the children about topic 19 (salt from the sea). Ask them if we could collect fresh water from the sea. Draw out that salt and other dissolved materials can be separated from water. Ask: *How can the water, instead of the salt, be collected?*

❑ Ask the children to look at the photograph. *How might these devices collect water from the sea?*

❑ *Can they can see any water inside the plastic containers? How do they think it gets there?* Remind them of their previous learning about evaporation. Ask: *What factors make water evaporate?* Point out that the heat of the Sun makes water from the sea evaporate into the air, and that this evaporated water is collected on the sides of the floating containers and runs into a small reservoir. *Is this water salty?*

Activities

● The children could set up a solar still (see *Photocopiable sheet* 7) and test the collected water (without tasting: ie, by evaporating it) to find out if it contains dissolved material.

● They could plan a safe test to find out if water evaporated from seawater and then collected as condensation contains salt. Condensed water could be

left to evaporate on a clean transparent dish, such as a petri dish or watch glass. *Does any dissolved material appear on the dish?* Compare this with a control in which sea water is left to evaporate. The children could use a strong magnifying glass or microscope to examine any materials left in the dish.

● The solar still works best in sunlight, but the children could investigate how well it works in different weather conditions. They could record the maximum and minimum temperatures on the days when they test it, and measure the amount of water collected over a 24-hour period. *What factors should they keep the same for a fair test?* (The site of the solar still, the length of time it is left.) They could try other ways of collecting water: for example, fastening plastic bags around leafy branches.

Higher-achieving children
If possible, arrange for a local university's chemistry department to analyse the water collected in the solar still. The children could send a sample in a sterilised container, along with a covering letter, to find out if the water is drinkable.

Lower-achieving children
They could also test water which has evaporated from clean saltwater and collected as condensation to see if it contains salt.

Plenary session

◆ Ask the children what they have learned about condensed water. Discuss the practical applications of their results: for example, for survival in arid places and for providing water on a small scale in hot countries with coasts, but a scarcity of water inland.

Vocabulary

dissolve, condensation, condense, evaporate, evaporation, liquid, separate, solar still, solid, solution

More about dissolving

21 Stalactites and stalagmites

Photo Book reference Page 24

QCA links
The children use their learning about dissolving and evaporation to explain a phenomenon they observe. (QCA Unit 6C)

Background information

The Cheddar caves were formed when limestone was worn away by underground streams and rivers. Stalactites form on the roofs of the caves when water containing dissolved calcium from the limestone (calcium carbonate), trickles through the rock and evaporates, depositing some of the calcium dissolved in it. Water dripping on to the floor of the cave deposits calcium and builds up stalagmites.

Starting point

■ Ask the children what they know about rock. *How does the weather affect rock?* Show them examples or pictures of rock which has been worn away by rain and by streams or rivers carrying particles of stone. *Where does the rock go?* Link this with work in geography on rivers.

Using the picture

❑ Ask the children if they know which are stalactites and which are stalagmites. They could make up mnemonics: for example, *stalactite contains c for ceiling, stalagmite contains g for ground, stalactites have to hang on tight and stalagmites might one day grow to reach them, stalagmites have far to grow.*

❑ Ask them if they know where Cheddar is. They could locate the area on a map, and find out from information books, or the Internet, about the types of rock found there.

❑ *What do they know about limestone?* Discuss their ideas about how stalactites and stalagmites might have been formed.

Activities

● Ask the children to put some limestone chippings into a plastic jar with a lid, add some water and shake them. *What are their observations? Does any of the limestone dissolve?*

● Ask them to repeat this, using white vinegar instead of water. *What do they notice happening? Does any of the limestone dissolve? What else happens?* Discuss whether this is a reversible change or whether a new material is formed. Ask: *What is the new material? Can the dissolved material be reclaimed from the vinegar?*

● Provide other materials which the children could test in the same way as the limestone chippings: for example, marble chippings, pieces of bone and teeth (boiled to sterilise them), sand, chalk, washing soda, glass marbles. *Photocopiable sheet 8* provides a chart, on which they can record their results. Discuss what is in the bubbles which makes the fizz, and where it comes from. Draw out that a new material has been made (a gas – carbon dioxide) and so, this is an irreversible change.

Higher-achieving children
They could find out about other places which have stalagmites and stalactites and check what type of rock is present there.

Lower-achieving children
Remind them of their previous work on dissolved salt, which can be reclaimed from water (topic 19). Explain that calcium also dissolves in water but that once the water evaporates, calcium forms solids which do not crumble as easily as pieces of salt.

Plenary session

◆ Draw out that when water evaporates any solid material which was dissolved in it remains and that this material can build up large deposits over the years.

Vocabulary

calcium, dissolve, evaporate, insoluble, irreversible, limestone, marble, reversible, soda, soluble, solution, stalactite, stalagmite

Reversible and irreversible changes

22 Fizz

Photo Book reference Page 25

QCA links
The children learn that mixing materials can cause them to change. They make careful observations and record and explain them using scientific knowledge and understanding. (QCA Unit 6D)

Background information

When a carbonate is mixed with an acid solution it produces carbon dioxide. The gas in fizzy drinks is carbon dioxide, which is compressed into the bottle or can and dissolves in the drink. When the lid is opened a fizzing sound can be heard; this is carbon dioxide escaping into the air.

Starting point

■ Review the children's previous learning about dissolving. *Which materials do they know dissolve in water?* Ask: *How can we tell that they have dissolved? What does the water look like after the materials have dissolved in it?*

Using the picture

❑ Ask the children what the picture shows. *Are the materials solid, liquid or gas? What is in the bubbles in the liquid? How could they have been made?*

❑ Ask them what they would do to make bubbles in a glass of water. *If they blew air into the water through a straw would the bubbles last as long as they do in a fizzy drink?* Discuss what happens to a fizzy drink which is left uncovered. Ask: *What do we mean when we describe a fizzy drink as 'flat'? What happens to the gas bubbles in it?*

Activities

● The children could compare still and sparkling water, using all appropriate senses. They could complete a comparison chart of similarities and differences.

● Ask them if they can think of anything which can be mixed with water to make it fizz. They could read the labels of bottles of sparkling water for clues. *What do they think* carbonated *means?*

● Provide a tub of sodium bicarbonate and let the children read the label. *Could this make still water fizz?* Let them try it and record their observations. Repeat this with baking powder. *If they evaporate the water, will they be able to get the baking powder or sodium bicarbonate back, or has a new material been made? How can we tell?*

● Ask: *What is the difference between sodium bicarbonate and baking powder?* The children should notice from the labels that baking powder contains an acid, while bicarbonate of soda does not. *Which gas do the children think is in the bubbles in sparkling water?* Draw attention to the clue in the word *carbonated* on the label.

● Ask them if they know of other materials which fizz when added to water: examples include Alka-Seltzer and Epsom salts: let the children try mixing these with water.

 Close supervision is required. Warn the children not to taste Alka-Seltzer or Epsom salts.

Higher-achieving children
They could plan a way of making still water fizzy, using sodium bicarbonate. Remind them of the difference between sodium bicarbonate and baking powder. *What is the 'missing' ingredient? What acid food could they add?* Examples include lemon, lime, orange or grape juice, or vinegar. Ask them to try their idea and record their results.

Lower-achieving children
Remind them of their previous work on yeast. Ask: *What made a balloon inflate when it was placed over the end of a bottle containing yeast, warm water and sugar?* (Gases – mainly carbon dioxide.) *Could they inflate a balloon with sodium bicarbonate or baking powder, mixed with water?*

Plenary session

◆ Draw out that some materials fizz when mixed with water – a new material has been made because part of the material has escaped as a gas. Point out that new materials can be made without a gas being given off.

Vocabulary

acid, baking powder, carbonated, carbon dioxide, fizz, gas, sodium bicarbonate, solution

23 Scones

Photo Book reference Page 26

QCA links
The children learn that mixing and heating some materials can cause them to change. They make careful observations and record and explain them using scientific knowledge and understanding. (QCA Unit 6D)

Background information

In a physical change, such as a change of state or dissolving, the nature of the particles (atoms or molecules) of a material stays the same and the materials can be returned to their previous state. A chemical change involves the combination of materials, or a change which cannot be reversed; new materials are formed and the original materials cannot easily be returned to their previous state.

Starting point

■ Review the children's previous learning about reversible and irreversible changes. Ask them if the following are reversible or irreversible changes: water → ice, steam → water, milk → butter, dried yeast + sugar + warm water → frothy yeast mixture. *How do they know?* Draw out that if a new material is made the change is not easily reversed.

Using the picture

❑ Ask the children what changes took place when the ingredients were mixed. *What materials were mixed? Which of these materials changed?* Discuss the ways in which the materials changed. Ask: *Have they combined with others to make new materials or have they remained separate but changed in some way? Can any of the materials be separated from the raw mixture? How?*

❑ *What changes took place when the scone mixture was baked (heated to 220°C)?* Discuss whether these changes are reversible or irreversible. Ask: *Was a new material made? Can any materials be separated from the cooked mixture?*

Activities

● The children could use the recipe to bake scones. Ask: *Would the ingredients change in the same ways if they were heated to 220°C without first being mixed? Would they change at all?* They could find out and record their observations on a chart:

Changes after heating and cooling enough for safety				
Material	Appearance	Smell	Taste	Feel
Flour				
Baking powder				
Sugar				
Raisins				
Butter				
Egg			⚠ Do not taste raw.	
Milk				

● *Which materials when heated separately changed in ways which can be reversed? Which ones changed irreversibly?*

Higher-achieving children
Ask: *Could scones be made by heating the materials separately and then mixing them?* They could try this and compare the results.

Lower-achieving children
Provide a ready-made table (see above) and show them how to complete it. A word bank could help. Encourage them to use the words *reversible* and *irreversible*.

Plenary session

◆ Draw out that when they are heated some materials change in ways which can be reversed (remind the children about changes of state: melting, evaporation, condensation and freezing). Contrast this with irreversible changes; those which occur when certain materials are mixed and when certain materials are heated: for example, flour, egg.

Vocabulary

chemical change, gas, irreversible, liquid, solid, reaction, reversible

Reversible and irreversible changes

24 A mixture to separate

Photo Book reference Page 27

QCA links
The children use their scientific knowledge and understanding to solve a problem. (QCA Unit 6D

Background information

The beads can be separated from the mixture by using a sieve. All the other materials will pass through a sieve. The iron filings can be separated by using a magnet (wrapped in paper or cling film, or placed in a small plastic bag, because iron filings are difficult to remove from a magnet). The remaining mixture of sand and salt can be mixed with water and filtered. Sand is not soluble and so it does not pass through the filter. Salt, which is soluble, passes through the filter along with the added water. The salt solution can then be left in a shallow dish for the water to evaporate – leaving the salt.

Starting point

■ Tell the children that they are going to be given a problem to solve, using what they have learned in recent science lessons and lessons from earlier years.

Using the picture

❑ Ask the children if a new material has been formed in this mixture. *Can the objects and materials be separated?*
❑ *What do the children know about separating pieces of material of different sizes? Which materials could be separated using a sieve?*
❑ Discuss which objects or materials would be difficult to separate, and why. *What do the children know about iron filings?* Ask: *What kind of material is iron? In what ways is it different from many other metals?* Draw out that it is magnetic.
❑ *How are salt and sand similar?* (The granules have similar sizes.) *How are they different?* (Apart from their colour and texture, salt is soluble but sand is not.) Ask: *Could they be separated using a sieve? Could they be separated using a filter? With what could they be mixed first? What would pass through a filter? What would not pass through a filter, and why?*

Activities

● Ask the children to work in groups to discuss how they can separate the materials in the mixture. *In which order should they be separated, and why?*
● Ask them to write their plan (numbering the stages in which each material will be separated from the others), including a list of materials and equipment, and an explanation of each stage. **Photocopiable sheet 9** provides a format for a flow chart which will help the children to plan how to separate the materials in the mixture.

Higher-achieving children
They could try separating a mixture similar to the one in the photograph but with the addition of steel ball bearings and marbles of a similar size.

Lower-achieving children
Take them through the procedure, step by step if necessary, giving clues as to the order in which the materials and objects should be separated: for example, *Which objects could be separated from the mixture using a sieve?* Show them a sieve and ask which objects will not pass through it. *What will be left in the mixture?* Ask them how they can separate sand and salt after mixing them with water, and so on, until all the materials are separated.

Plenary session

◆ Ask the children to share their plans before they try them out. Discuss why the iron filings should be separated from the mixture before water is added. Ask: *What happens to iron when it is wet?*

Vocabulary

dissolve, filter, insoluble, magnet, magnetic, sieve, soluble, solution

Reversible and irreversible changes

Photo Book reference *Page 28*

25 Central heating

QCA links
The children learn that some materials are changed by burning and that the change is irreversible. They use a model in order to answer a scientific question. (QCA Unit 6D)

Background information

The central heating boiler creates reversible and irreversible changes. Gas is burned (irreversible), cold water is heated (reversible), hot water in radiators cools (reversible), waste gases are produced (irreversible). An oil-fired, solid fuel-fired or electrically-powered system could be analysed in a similar way. Solid fuel and oil change irreversibly when they are burned but electricity is not changed because it is not a material.

Starting point

■ Ask the children if they can name the main materials which change when the school central heating system is switched on. (Water or air becomes hot.) *Is this change reversible?* (Yes – hot air and hot water can be cooled.) Fuel is burned. *Is this reversible?* (No – gases and other waste products are produced.) Tell the children that they are going to find out about some of the fuels used for heating water and to consider the changes to the fuels.

Using the pictures

❑ With the children, read the captions and discuss what happens in each picture. Ask them to complete the flow chart in **Photocopiable sheet 10** to describe the central heating system shown in the photographs.
❑ Ask them which change is reversible. *Can they identify an irreversible change?*

Activities

● Ask the children what change central heating radiators cause. *What do they heat?* (Air.) *Can this change be reversed?* They could find out about the effect of a radiator on the air in a room, using a model:

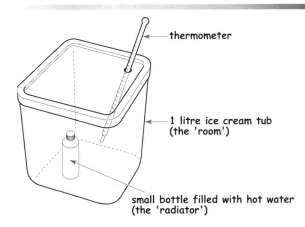

The effects of a radiator on the air in a room.

● **Photocopiable sheet 10** provides a flow chart on which the children can describe the stages of the processes involved in a central heating system (see Starting point). They can use this in relation to the system shown in the photographs and the one used in the school. Ask them to identify any materials which are changed, and whether these changes are reversible or irreversible.

Higher-achieving children
They could use the model to compare the effects of different sized radiators in a room.

Lower-achieving children
Before the lesson, discuss the children's experiences of fuels which are burned: for example, a gas hob or a gas fire.

Plenary session

◆ Draw out that gas or oil can be burned as fuel, and that this process produces new materials – an irreversible change. Heating and cooling water are reversible changes (even if the water evaporates or freezes).

Vocabulary

boiler, burn, change, convert, energy, flue, fuel, fumes, gas, heat, liquid

Reversible and irreversible changes

Photo Book reference Page 29

26 Burning

QCA links
The children learn that the changes which occur when most materials are burned are irreversible. They learn to recognise and assess hazards and risks in burning materials. (QCA Unit 6D)

Background information

Burning (known as *combustion*) is a change involving a chemical reaction between a material: for example, wood, coal, gas, oil and oxygen.

Starting point

■ Remind the children about the changes involved in the central heating system (topic 25). Ask them what was burned and how it changed. *Can they think of any other materials which burn?* Ask them which parts of a building would burn and which would not if the building caught fire.

Using the pictures

❑ Ask the children to tell the story of the pictures with a partner, including how it might have begun. Invite feedback. Focus on the changes taking place. Ask: *What are the sofa and armchairs made of? How do they change as they burn? Are the changes reversible? What will remain after the fire?* Draw out that fabric and wood burn but metal does not; any metal parts will remain: for example, castors, springs, nails and screws.

❑ Ask the children what new material they can see being produced. (Smoke, consisting of gases and particles of burnt material.) *Is this a reversible change?*

❑ Discuss the possible causes of the fire and ask what the children know about keeping safe from fire: dangers include playing with matches, lighters and fireworks; also, candles placed near flammable materials; and unattended pans, especially those containing fat, such as chip pans. Explain that the fumes from fires, as well as the flames themselves, can kill.

Activities

● If local authority and school guidelines permit the use of naked flames the children could test some materials to find out how easily they catch fire. This is an opportunity for them to be involved in risk management.

● Use very small pieces of wood, paper, card, metal foil, string, wool, pieces of metal and ceramics:

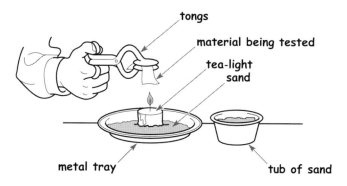

Safe burning of materials in the classroom.

 Do not burn rubber or plastic, which can give off harmful fumes. Long hair must be tied back.

● The children could record the results on a chart on which they describe any changes which take place and whether they are reversible.

● They could write instructions for the safe testing of materials for burning.

Higher-achieving children
They could also find out from the Internet about fire safety precautions for current festivals or celebrations in which fire or lights are used: for example, Christmas, Divali, Guy Fawkes' Night, Halloween, Hanukkah, Holi.

Lower-achieving children
Before the lesson, show them the remains of a bonfire (or a picture of one). *What has been burned and why are these materials left?*

Plenary session

◆ Draw out the dangers of fire, as well as the irreversible changes which occur.

Vocabulary

burn, combustion, flames, foam, fumes, hazard, heat, metal, safety, smoke, wood

Reversible and irreversible changes

Photo Book reference Page 30

27 Putting out a fire

QCA links
The children learn to recognise and assess hazards and risks in burning materials. (QCA Unit 6D)

Background information

If the oxygen supply to a fire is removed the fire will stop burning. Fire blankets, foam and water cover a fire, keeping out oxygen. Fire blankets are suitable only for small fires. The larger the fire, the more foam or water is required.

Starting point

■ The children should first have completed topic 26. Discuss the fire safety strategies they suggested. Ask: *How could sand or water be used for putting out a small fire? In what ways are the effects of water and sand similar?* (They cover the fire.)

Using the picture

❏ Ask the children to describe each method of extinguishing a fire and how it works. Discuss why covering a fire with a blanket, foam or water puts it out. Explain that oxygen (from the air) is needed for a fire to burn; if a fire is starved of oxygen it will go out. Also, wet materials do not burn as easily as dry ones.

❏ Ask: *Why are the firefighters wearing helmets with visors? What is special about their clothing?* Draw out that the helmets protect their heads from falling and burning materials and the visors shield their faces from heat, as well as protecting them from sparks and debris. The suits are made of fire-resistant material and insulated to give protection from heat.

❏ Discuss what the fire-fighter using foam has strapped to his back. Explain that breathing apparatus helps if the firefighter is surrounded by fumes and smoke. Remind the children of the dangers of fumes from fires.

Activities

● If possible, arrange a visit to a fire station. Before the visit, help the children to prepare questions about smoke, fumes, extinguishing fires, fire safety and how materials change when they burn.

● Burn a small piece of combustible material (see topic 26), and show the children how the flames can be put out using a piece of thick cloth, water or sand. Draw out that the fire cannot burn because the water, sand or cloth keep air out and that it needs oxygen in order to burn. Explain how someone whose clothes have caught fire could be helped. (By rolling him or her in a blanket or carpet.)

● If a visit is not possible, or as a follow-up or preparation for a visit, show the children a video about fire safety (see **Resources**). They could make posters based on what they have learned. Different groups could focus on a different aspect of fire safety at home: for example, smoke alarms, escape routes, fire prevention (candles, cookers and pans, electricity), what to do if there is a fire (for example, calling the fire brigade, checking doors to see if they are hot before attempting to open them).

Higher-achieving children
Provide four tea-lights, standing in small trays of sand. Before lighting them and covering three of them with clear glass jars of different sizes, explain what you are going to do and ask the children to predict the order in which the tea lights will go out, and why. Discuss why none of the tea lights under the jars continues to burn as long as the one without a jar. They could write a report about the investigation.

Lower-achieving children
They could draw and write a picture story about a fire which is put out using one of the methods they have discussed. Point out that children should always seek the help of an adult if there is a fire.

Plenary session

◆ Draw out that burning is a chemical reaction in which oxygen is used and that irreversible changes are made to a material.

Vocabulary

breathing apparatus, burn, extinguish, extinguisher, fireproof, flames, foam, fumes, heat, heatproof, insulated, oxygen, safety, smoke, water

28 Gravity in space

Photo Book reference Page 31

QCA links
The children learn that the Earth and objects are pulled towards one another, and that this gravitational force causes objects to have weight. (QCA Unit 6E)

Background information

Masses, such as the Earth and the Moon, are attracted to one another by their gravitational forces. The larger a mass, the greater the gravitational force it exerts. Astronauts bounce as they walk on the Moon because it has a much smaller mass than the Earth and, therefore, has a much smaller gravitational pull. The planets and their satellites were set in motion by a huge force. Once an object starts moving it continues to do so unless a force acts against this movement. There is no air and, therefore, no friction in space to act against the movement of the planets. The gravitational pull of the Sun, because of its huge mass, is strong enough to keep the planets orbiting around it (they would move in a straight line otherwise). Similarly, the Earth's gravitational pull is strong enough to keep the Moon orbiting around it. Once an artificial satellite is launched into space it continues to move and the Earth's gravitational pull keeps it orbiting.

Starting point

■ Ask the children to complete a concept map about gravity; include the words: *Earth, force, gravity, Moon, planets, pull, space*. They could repeat this at the end of the unit of work and compare the two concept maps to assess what they have learned.

Using the pictures

❏ Point out that this diagram is not to scale because of the enormous size of the Sun. Ask the children to describe the movement of the planets. *What makes them orbit the Sun?* Write up their responses. Point out the Earth and ask the children what they can see orbiting it (the Moon and many small items which have been drawn to represent artificial satellites).

❏ Explain that the lower picture has been drawn to represent a closer view of the Earth with its Moon and artificial satellites. The illustration is not to scale in order to show some satellites in detail. Ask the children how the artificial satellites have been put into orbit around the Earth, why they keep moving and what keeps them in orbit. *Why do they not go off into space or crash to Earth?* Point out the spaceship launching a satellite and explain that once a satellite begins moving in a straight line above the Earth's atmosphere there is nothing to stop it moving but that the pull of the Earth's gravity keeps it in orbit.

Activities

● Use a simulation to explore how gravity acts on objects in orbit. Tie a tennis ball into a sock and attach it securely to a piece of strong cord. Ue the cord to swing the ball in 'orbit' around themselves. Discuss how to make the ball move away from them (let go of the cord) and what keeps it orbiting (the pull on the cord). Draw out that the Earth's gravitational pull acts in a similar way on objects which orbit it. They could draw and write a report about the investigation.

● The children could use information books to find out about the gravitational force of other planets. Ask them what it would be like if they could go to Venus, Pluto, Mercury, Jupiter or Saturn.

Higher-achieving children
Ask them to use information books or the Internet, to find out more about satellites in space. They could write some questions to which they would like answers: for example, *What are satellites used for? At what speed do they orbit the Earth? How long does a satellite take to complete an orbit? Do they move at different speeds? Do satellites crash down to Earth? Can they be brought back?* They could organise a 'Question and answer' board about satellites.

Lower-achieving children
If necessary, review their previous learning about forces. Explain that gravity is a force, pulling masses towards one another rather like the pull of a magnet.

Plenary session

◆ Explain that gravity acts in space but the farther away from a planet, the weaker the force; the larger a mass, the greater its gravitational pull.

Vocabulary

Earth, force, gravitational pull, gravity, mass, Moon, orbit, planet, satellite, Sun, weight

Forces in action

29 Boats

QCA links
The children learn that water provides an upward force (upthrust) on a submerged object. They make careful measurements and present results in tables. (QCA Unit 6E)

Background information

An object placed in water displaces some of the water. If the weight of the displaced water is as great as that of the object, the object floats. A force equal to the weight of the displaced water pushes upwards against the object, making it float. A heavy metal boat can float because it displaces its own weight in water.

Starting point

■ Begin with the picture story *Mr Archimedes' Bath* (see **Resources**). Point out that the story is meant for much younger children but that the scientific ideas in it are quite difficult. Ask the children why the water level rose. *Why did some slop over the sides of the bath? Which animal caused it? What happened if they all got in at once? Why? Would this happen if they slid into the water very carefully?* Introduce the word *displacement* for water pushed out of place by an immersed object.

Using the pictures

❑ Ask the children what the canoe is made of. *Does it displace water?* Ask them what the ferry boat is made of. *Does it displace water? Which displaces more water – the canoe or the ferry boat?* Ask the children if the boats would displace the same amount of water, more water or less water, if there were more people in them.

❑ Ask them if a cube of metal will float (a volunteer could demonstrate this). *Why does it sink? Can the children explain why a metal ferry boat floats?*

Activities

● Ask the children how they could measure the amount of water displaced when they get into a bath. They could try out their idea by immersing a can of food in a basin filled to the brim with water and placed in a bowl to collect the displaced water. Use a measuring jug or measuring cylinder to measure the volume of the water, and compare the volumes of water displaced by different (non-floating) objects, such as cans of food of different sizes.

● *Photocopiable sheet 11* shows the children how to measure the amounts of water displaced by empty soft drinks cans, and others containing different amounts of sand (with the hole sealed). They should weigh the cans and the displaced water, measure the volume of water displaced and record whether the can floated. *What do the children notice about the weights of the floating cans and the water they displaced?* Ask them to work in groups to devise a rule about objects which float.

Higher-achieving children
Compare the volume of water displaced by blocks (of identical sizes) of different materials: for example, metal, wood (such as balsa, pine and mahogany), polystyrene and other plastics. Whether the materials sink, or the level at which they float, depends on the volume of water they displace. Denser floating objects float lower in the water and displace more water than less dense ones.

Lower-achieving children
Review their previous learning about floating and help them to draw conclusions. Discuss why hollow objects float better than solid ones of the same material.

Plenary session

◆ Draw out that objects which float displace their own weight in water.

Vocabulary

displace, displacement, float, force, gravity, immerse, upthrust, weight

Forces in action

30 The Plimsoll line

QCA links

The children learn that when an object is submerged in water the water provides an upward force (upthrust) on it. They make observations and use tables to present results. (QCA Unit 6E)

Background information

A ship displaces water. If the weight of the displaced water is as great as the weight of the ship, the ship floats. A force equal to the weight of the displaced water pushes upward against the ship, making it float. A ship carrying a cargo floats lower in the water than an empty one; this level is affected by the temperature of the water and the amount of salt in it. A 19th-century naval admiral, named Samuel Plimsoll, devised a system for marking the sides of ships to show safe water levels in salt, fresh, warm and cold water.

Starting point

■ Read *Who Sank the Boat?* and ask the children which animal sank the boat. *How can they tell? How could an animal as small as the mouse sink a boat? Would the mouse have sunk the boat if it had got in first?* Discuss how the cow could have sunk it by putting too much weight at one end, but managed to keep it afloat by moving towards the centre. Ask: *Does the boat displace water?*

Using the pictures

❑ Ask the children to explain the markings on the sides of ships. *What clues can they find in the photographs?*
❑ Explain that the letters have the following meanings: TF (tropical fresh water), T (tropics), F (fresh water), S (summer), W (winter), WNA (winter North Atlantic). LR stands for Lloyds Register (the organisation which regulates world shipping). Discuss the differences between the water in different places and at different times of the year. *How is seawater different from fresh water?*

Activities

● Provide margarine tubs or boats with hollow hulls. Ask the children to estimate how many wooden cubes (of the same size), or other suitable objects, could be placed in the boat without sinking it. *What will happen to the boat as more cubes or objects are added? Does it matter where they are placed?* The children could draw pictures to show how they will load the boat, and predict what will happen. Let them test their ideas and record the results.

● They could use a waterproof marker to mark the water level on the side of the boat when different masses are placed in it: 50, 100, 150 grams, and so on.

Higher-achieving children
They could plan an investigation to find out how fresh, salt, warm or cold water affects the levels at which a boat floats and record their findings on a graph:

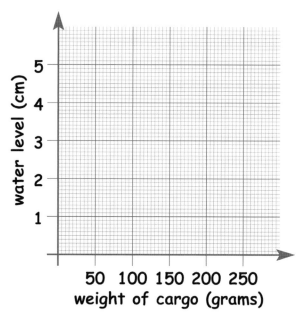

Lower-achieving children
Review what floats and what sinks, and help the children to draw conclusions. Discuss why objects made of certain materials float better than others, and why hollow objects float better than solid ones of the same material.

Plenary session

◆ Draw out that objects float if they are less dense (lighter for their size) than water or if they displace their own weight in water. Also draw out the importance of balance.

Vocabulary

displace, float, force, gravity, upthrust, weight

Forces in action

31 Parachuting

QCA links
The children learn that air resistance slows down moving objects and that when an object falls air resistance acts in the opposite direction to the weight of the object. (QCA Unit 6E)

Background information

Falling objects are affected by forces such as gravity and air resistance. Gravity pulls an object downwards, towards the Earth; air resistance exerts an upward force on the object. Contrary to everyday common-sense observations, gravity gives all objects the same acceleration, whatever their mass. If gravity were the only force acting on falling objects, light objects would fall at the same speed as heavy ones. Air resistance depends on the shape of the object. The more air trapped beneath the object, the greater the force of air resistance.

Starting points

■ Ask the children what happens to an object if they drop it. *Why does it fall to the ground?* Review their previous learning about gravity.

■ Hold a flat sheet of paper and ask the children if it will fall straight downwards. Drop the paper and ask them why it did not fall straight downwards.

Using the picture

❑ Discuss the purpose of a parachute. *How does it help the person to land safely from a great height?* Ask the children to use the picture to help them to explain their ideas. They could focus on the difference in shape between a parachute packed in a bag, lying on the ground and descending through the air. Draw out that the parachute fills with air. Point out the parts of the parachute which are visibly pushed upwards by the air.

Activities

● Ask the children what difference is made by the size of a parachute. *Does a larger parachute always make an object fall more slowly than a small one?*

● They could investigate the effects of using different sized parachutes, made from plastic sheeting, to slow down the fall of an object such as a cork.

● Ask them to make a graph on which to record their results and to draw conclusions from these results about the effect of the size of the parachute.

Higher-achieving children
Ask them to design a parachute to make a cork land at the same time as a sheet of paper dropped at the same time, from the same height.

Lower-achieving children
Help them to make parachutes of different sizes and ask them to predict the effect they will have on a falling cork. *Which will make it drop the most slowly?*

Plenary session

◆ Draw out that a parachute slows the fall of an object because it traps more air beneath it than would the object without a parachute, and that the upward force of air on an object acts in the opposite direction to gravity.

Vocabulary

air resistance, force, gravity, mass, opposite, parachute, weight

32 Sunbeams

Photo Book reference Page 35

QCA links

The children learn that light travels from a source and use their knowledge about light to explain observations. They use straight lines, with arrows, to indicate the direction of a beam, or ray, of light travelling from a source. (QCA Unit 6F)

Background information

When light travels from a source (such as the Sun, a candle or a torch) and hits an object it can be reflected, absorbed by the object or pass through it. Opaque materials absorb or reflect light; light can pass through transparent or translucent materials. Translucent materials reflect or absorb more light than do transparent ones. All objects we see reflect some light – otherwise we would not see them.

Starting point

■ Ask the children to name some light sources. Ask: *What does the light from the Sun pass through on its way to Earth? What can block the Sun's light?* Discuss what happens when light is blocked. (Shadows are formed.)

Using the picture

❏ Discuss whether sunlight passes through clouds. (If none passed through clouds there would be complete darkness.) Review the children's understanding of *opaque, translucent* and *transparent*. Ask: *Are clouds opaque, translucent or transparent?*

❏ *What happens to any sunlight which does not pass through clouds?* It cannot disappear. Children who have travelled by air might have noticed the brightness of reflected sunlight off the upper surface of clouds. This can be seen in the photograph. Also, point out that some light is absorbed by the clouds.

❏ *What can they learn from the photograph about rays of light?* (They travel in straight lines.) Discuss why some parts of the sky are brighter than others. (More light passes through where there are gaps in the clouds or where the clouds are less dense.)

Activities

● Punch holes, at random, in a tin can. Stand a candle in a secure holder in a tray of sand. Turn out the classroom light. There is no need to darken the room but if there are blinds or curtains, they could be drawn.

● Light the candle and place the can over it. Shake some talcum powder into the air around it. *What do the children notice? In what way does this remind them of the sunlight coming through the clouds in the photograph?*

● Ask them where the light comes from and where it goes. *How far do they think it travels?* If they think there is a point at which it stops, ask them what stops it. Encourage them to ask their own questions about their observations: for example, *Do rays of light bend or are they straight? How can we tell? What blocks some of the light from the candle? What happens to this light?*

● Remove the can from the candle and ask the children in which directions the light is travelling from the candle. They could draw labelled diagrams to show this and what happens when the tin can is placed over the candle. They could include arrows to show the direction of the light.

Higher-achieving children
They could find a way of measuring the brightness of torchlight at different distances. *Why does it become less bright farther from the torch?* Ask them to draw conclusions about their results.

Lower-achieving children
It might be helpful if they first have an opportunity to experiment with making shadows, using a torch and a piece of card.

Plenary session

◆ Draw out that light travels in all directions from a source unless it is blocked. It does not stop but becomes fainter as it spreads out over a greater distance.

Vocabulary

absorb, beam, block, brightness, opaque, ray, reflect, shadow, source, translucent, transparent

How we see things

33 The eye

Photo Book reference Page 36

QCA links
The children learn that we see things because light from a source is reflected from them and enters our eyes. (QCA Unit 6F)

Background information

Rays of light from the Sun and other sources, hit objects, are reflected from them and enter our eyes through the pupils, which are openings in the centre of the iris (the coloured part of the eye) and create images on the retina. Nerves from the eyes send messages to the brain, which interprets them.

Starting points

■ The children should first have completed topic 32. Remind them about their observations of the candle. Light the candle again and ask them how they think they can see the light from it. Draw out that light from the candle enters our eyes.

■ Extinguish the candle using an inverted can and ask the children if they can still see it. Point out that we see things when light enters our eyes. *Where does the light come from which helps us to see the candle?* Remind the children of earlier work on the eye, when they placed objects in boxes with spy-holes and could only see them when holes in the boxes were uncovered. Review this if they have forgotten it:

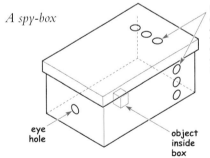

A spy-box

light holes (cover them with card and uncover them, one at a time, until enough light enters the box to show what is inside it)

eye hole

object inside box

Using the picture

❑ Ask the children to discuss what they can see in the photograph and to write a description of the eye. Invite feedback. Supply the names of parts of the eye, if necessary, and ask the children to draw a labelled diagram of a partner's eye, using magnifying glasses to help in their observations.

❑ Ask them how they think light enters the eye. They might not be aware that the pupils are openings covered by transparent material.

⚠ Warn the children not to touch one another's eyes.

Activities

● They could observe what happens to one another's pupils when they open their eyes after they have been closed for a while and when they look towards a window (not directly towards the Sun). Use a scale of spots of increasing size to measure and compare the sizes of the pupils:

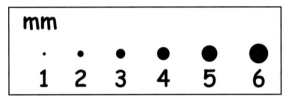

'Spots scale'

Higher-achieving children
They could investigate images made when light reflected from objects passes through a biconvex lens on to a screen. Explain that there is a similar lens inside the eye and that images appear upside down on it and are interpreted by the brain.

Lower-achieving children
Help them to draw labelled diagrams showing the directions in which light travels from a source to an object, and then to the eye.

Plenary session

◆ Explain that light is reflected from objects and enters our eyes through the pupils. Volunteers who have completed the extension activity could present an explanation of what happens inside the eye.

Vocabulary

beam, block, brain, brightness, eyelash, eyelid, image, iris, message, nerve, pupil, ray, reflect, source

34 Useful mirrors

QCA links
The children learn that when a beam of light is reflected from a surface its direction changes. They make careful observations and comparisons. (QCA Unit 6F)

Background information

A beam of light reflected from a mirror continues in a different direction. This extremely uniform type of reflection creates an image. A plane (flat) mirror reflects beams of light at an angle equal to the one at which they hit the mirror.

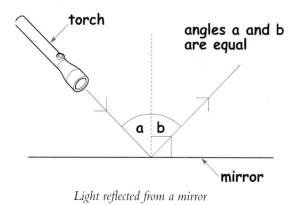

Light reflected from a mirror

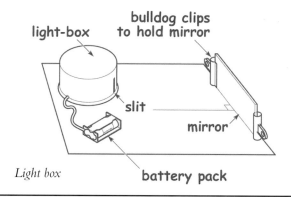

Light box

 Use plastic mirrors or cover the backs of glass mirrors with adhesive material and tape the edges.

- They could then remove the mirror, fold the paper along the line which is at right angles to the mirror, and compare the angle at which the beam hit the mirror with the angle at which it was reflected. Ask: *What do they notice? Does this happen if the angle of the light-box or torch is changed?*
- Challenge them to make the reflected beam follow the same path as the beam from the light-box or torch. (The beam will be at right angles to the mirror).

Higher-achieving children
Ask them to find a way of using mirrors to reflect a beam of light around the outside of a box and back to its source.

Lower-achieving children
They could investigate their own reflections in mirrors. Ask them to touch their right ear, while looking in a mirror. *What do they notice?* Help them to draw a diagram to show where the reflected light from their right ear hits the mirror.

Starting point

■ The children should first have completed topics 32 and 33. Remind them that they see objects because light is reflected from them.

Using the pictures

❑ Ask the children to discuss and make notes about the ways in which each mirror is useful. *Whom does the road mirror help, and how? How does a rear-view mirror help a driver? How does a dentist or a hairdresser use a mirror?*

❑ Draw out that light reflected from objects hits a mirror and forms images of the objects. Ask: *Does a mirror image look exactly the same as the object itself?* Draw out that a mirror image is reversed.

Activities

● Provide mirrors, pieces of white paper, card, torches or battery-powered light-boxes. Mirrors can be supported upright by bulldog clips or Plasticine. Ask the children to draw lines, using a ruler, along the beam of light from a torch or light-box to a mirror and along the reflected beam of light:

Plenary session

◆ Draw out that a beam of light is reflected from a mirror at an angle which is equal to the angle at which it hits the mirror.

Vocabulary

angle, beam, plane mirror, ray, reflect, source

How we see things

35 Reflectors (1)
36 Reflectors (2)

Photo Book reference Pages 38 and 39

QCA links
The children learn that shiny surfaces reflect light better than dull ones. They make and record comparisons of how different surfaces reflect light and draw conclusions from their observations. (QCA Unit 6F)

Background information

All objects we can see reflect light. Most of them scatter reflected light in all directions. Objects with very smooth surfaces reflect light in a uniform way. Light-coloured objects reflect more light than dark ones. The eyes of cats, and some other nocturnal animals, have an iridescent layer behind the retina and around the optic nerve, which acts like a mirror. Light passing into the animal's eyeball bounces off this iridescent layer, reflecting the incoming light within the eye, making the most of the light and enabling the animal to see in near (but not total) darkness. The eyes shine at night because the pupils are dilated wide enough for the iridescent layer to be visible. 'Cat's eyes' on roads are reflective glass beads in a rubber pad, fitted into a metal casing which is sunk into the surface of the road. Every time a wheel passes over the rubber pad it is pushed into its metal base and the reflective bead is wiped clean by the rubber, in the same way as the eyelid cleans the eye. Bicycle reflectors are composed of hundreds of tiny prisms, formed from sets of three tiny plastic mirrors meeting at angles to reflect incoming light back to its source (see Activities). Similarly, prisms are used in some reflective plastic strips. Others have tiny glass beads buried into a layer of plastic. The beads are not noticeable to the touch because they are covered with a layer of coloured plastic. When a light shines on the reflector the beads reflect light in all directions.

Starting point

■ The children should first have completed topics 32 to 34. Review their learning about reflections; draw out that we see images in a mirror because they reflect light, which is then reflected by the mirror.

Using the pictures

❏ Ask the children to discuss with a partner, and make notes about, the objects which show up in the dark. Remind them that nothing can be seen in total darkness.

❏ Ask them to think about what makes these objects show up more than everything else around them. *In what ways are they different?* The children could consider their texture, colour and the materials from which they are made.

Activities

● Set up a mirror as shown below and ask the children how many images of the model they can see:

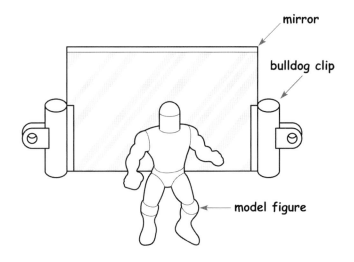

mirror

bulldog clip

model figure

  Use plastic mirrors, or cover the backs of glass mirrors with adhesive material, and tape the edges.

How we see things

35 Reflectors (1)
36 Reflectors (2)

Photo Book reference Pages 38 and 39

QCA links
The children learn that shiny surfaces reflect light better than dull ones. They make and record comparisons of how different surfaces reflect light, and draw conclusions from their observations. (QCA Unit 6F)

Activities (continued)

- Place two mirrors at an angle of 90°, as shown, and ask the children how many images of the figure they can see. Let them use a protractor to check the angle at which the mirrors meet.

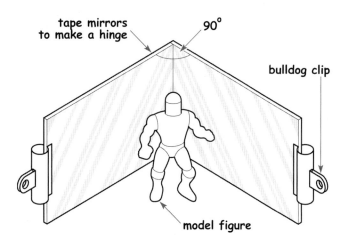

- Ask the children to investigate what happens when they alter the angle between the mirrors (30°, 45°, 60°, 120°). They could record their findings on a chart (see *Photocopiable sheet 12*).
- Show them how mirrors are used in bicycle reflectors (in prism formations):

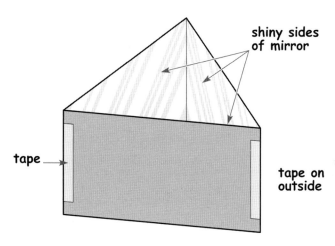

What can the children see when they look into the reflector?

- Let them investigate a bicycle reflector. Ask them to look at it from very close up. They should notice that it looks black because they see the inverted image of the pupil of the eye. If the tiny mirrors in the reflector were much bigger they would each reflect an image of the eye. Ask the children to look at the reflector while slowly moving the edge of a piece of white paper in front of the eye, stopping just before it blocks their vision. They should see small white reflections in the facets of the reflector. Explain that when light hits the reflector it is reflected back by each of the tiny corner cube reflectors.
- The children can stand mirrors on the lines marked on *Photocopiable sheet 12* and measure the angles as shown. This helps them to identify the relationship between the angle between the mirrors and the number of images they see.

Higher-achieving children
Ask them what pattern they notice in the number of reflected images in the two mirrors and the angle between the mirrors. They could also try mirrors placed at angles of 20°, 120° and 180°, and present their findings on a graph. If necessary, remind them of the number of degrees in a complete revolution (360°).

Lower-achieving children
They could investigate different surfaces to find out which ones reflect a torch beam and in which they can see their reflections. *What do they notice about the surfaces of those which reflect a torch beam and those which reflect images?* Ask them to find out what they need to do to a piece of transparent material to make it reflect images, and to explain why.

Plenary session

- Draw out that shiny surfaces reflect more light than matt ones; also, that when mirrors face one another light is reflected from one to the other.

Vocabulary

angle, beam, matt, mirror, ray, reflect, reflector, shiny, source

Changing circuits

37 Bulbs and batteries

QCA links
The children learn that the brightness of bulbs can be changed and that care needs to be taken when components in a circuit are changed, to ensure that bulbs do not burn out. (QCA Unit 6G)

Background information

Electrical energy can be converted to other forms. An electric light bulb converts electrical energy into heat, which gives off light. The brightness of a bulb depends on the temperature of the filament and the gas around it and on the amount of electrical current flowing through the bulb. The temperature and, therefore, the brightness can be increased by increasing the current (using a higher voltage battery).

The voltage indicated on a bulb is the voltage at which it works at optimum brightness. Using a slightly higher voltage battery shortens the life of the bulb. A much higher voltage burns it out because the filament can burn through. It is safe to use a battery up to 6V with a 4.5V bulb and a battery up to 4.5V with a 2.5V bulb.

 Never use car batteries in experiments. Do not use rechargeable batteries.

Starting point

■ Begin by showing the children a simple circuit consisting of a bulb in a holder, a battery in a battery-holder, connectors and wires. Ask them what they can do to make the bulb go out (they can break the circuit in various ways). Ask them what they know about electrical circuits.

Using the pictures

❑ Ask the children to work in pairs to decide which bulbs can be used with which batteries. Invite feedback. Ask: *Does it matter which batteries are used with each bulb?*

❑ Ask them to read the writing and numbers on the bulbs and batteries, and to discuss what it means. *Do they know what V means in electricity?* If necessary, explain that it means *voltage* – the measure of the electrical charge. It might be appropriate to explain that this means the flow of invisible, charged particles called *electrons*.

❑ Explain that although we call a single cell a *battery*, a battery is a series of more than one cell. Ask them what voltage is supplied by the batteries in each photograph. (The first is a 12V car battery; the second is a series of four 1.5V cells (6V) and the third is a pair of 1.5V cells (3V).) Draw out that the 3.5V bulb is best used with the 3V battery, the 6.5V bulb is best used with the 6V battery and the 12V bulb is best used with the 12V battery. Discuss why.

Activities

● The children could use magnifying glasses to read the voltages of a collection of bulbs. Ask them to match them to batteries.

● Ask them to try a bulb with batteries of different voltages (within safe limits) and to record their observations. They might remember from previous work how to measure the brightness of a bulb (counting the layers of thin paper through which it can be seen).

● They could also try adding a battery to a circuit after calculating whether this will be safe. Ask them to measure the brightness of the bulb when they do so.

Higher-achieving children
They could measure, and record on a graph, the effect of adding a bulb to a circuit.

Lower-achieving children
Ask them if large batteries provide a higher voltage than smaller ones. *Is this always the case?*

Plenary session

◆ Draw out that voltage is a measure of the flow of an electric current, and that if we know the voltage of a current we can match electrical devices such as bulbs to it.

Vocabulary

battery, brightness, bulb, cell, circuit, electron, filament, volt, voltage

Changing circuits

38 Brighter bulbs

Photo Book reference Page 41

QCA links
The children learn that care needs to be taken when components in a circuit are changed, to ensure that bulbs do not burn out. They make fair comparisons and draw conclusions. (QCA Unit 6G)

Background information

The voltage of mains electricity is between 220 and 240 volts. This is much higher than that of batteries. The highest voltage used by most battery-powered devices is 6 volts. These are safe for using with children. A car battery usually has a voltage of 12 volts. This is too high for use in primary schools. Bulbs are also marked in watts. A watt (W) is the unit for measuring electrical power (the rate of doing work – in this case, moving electrons around a circuit). Rates of doing other work are also measured in watts. A 150W bulb can work at a greater rate (and so burn more brightly) than a 100W or a 60W bulb using the same electrical current.

Starting point

■ The children should first have completed topic 37. Ask them what they know about the electric light bulbs they have used in circuits, and about voltage. *Do they know the difference between the voltages provided by the batteries in the circuits they used and the voltage of mains electricity?*

Using the pictures

❑ Ask the children to write the following labels on removable stickers and match them to the bulbs: energy-saving fluorescent lamp, regular light bulb, globe bulb, candle bulb, energy-saving bulb. They could also label the bulbs according to voltage and whether they are clear or pearl (opal).

❑ Remind them what *voltage* means and ask them what they notice about the voltage of the bulbs. Remind them of the voltages of batteries they have used and, if necessary, let them look at some batteries. *What were the voltages of the bulbs they used with batteries?* Discuss why the light bulbs in the photograph have a different voltage which is much higher than the ones they have used in experiments. Draw out that mains electricity has a much higher voltage than batteries, and that this makes it dangerous.

❑ The children might have heard of *wattage*. Explain that bulbs of a high wattage burn more brightly than those of a lower wattage if everything else is kept the same.

Activities

● The children could make a simple circuit with a 1.5V battery and try lighting different bulbs with it. Ask them to measure the brightness of the bulbs by counting the sheets of paper through which they can be seen and to record their results on a bar chart. They should repeat their measurements to check their accuracy. *Can they find any pattern in their results?* They could repeat this using a 3V battery and a 4.5V battery, or different groups could work with different batteries.

 Emphasise that children should never experiment with mains electricity.

Higher-achieving children
Ask them to find ways of changing the brightness of a bulb, without changing the battery.

Lower-achieving children
It might be necessary first to review what they have learned about batteries, including the significance of the *voltage* of bulbs.

Plenary session

◆ Draw out that light bulbs are designed to work from specific voltages.

Vocabulary

battery, brightness, bulb, cell, circuit, electron, filament, mains electricity, volt, voltage, watt, wattage

Changing circuits

39 Brighter, dimmer, louder, quieter

Photo Book reference Page 42

QCA links
The children learn that changing the wires in a circuit can change the brightness of a bulb or the volume of a bell or buzzer. (QCA Unit 6G)

Background information

A greater voltage (flow of electrons) makes a bulb brighter or a bell or buzzer louder. Resistance in the circuit acts against the flow of electrons. Energy is used in moving a current through the components of a circuit; they all have some resistance. The longer or thinner the wires, the greater the resistance. A dimmer switch and a volume control introduce resistance into a circuit in a way which can be controlled; they are known as *variable resistors*. They contain a coil of wire, or a strip of metal or conducting ceramic, connected to the circuit. When the knob is turned, it moves a piece of wire inside the switch to shorten or lengthen the part of the strip through which electricity flows. The longer this is, the greater the resistance.

Starting point

■ Ask the children to complete a concept map about what makes a bulb brighter or dimmer. *Do they think the same factors affect the loudness of a bell or buzzer?*

Using the pictures

❑ Discuss what a dimmer switch is for. Ask the children to discuss with a partner what they can see inside a dimmer switch. Ask them to discuss what effect it has, and how it works.

❑ Ask them to look at the pictures of a volume control switch and to describe what it is for. *What can they see inside it?* Ask them to discuss what effect it has, and how it works.

❑ The children could write explanations of the two switches. Invite feedback and draw out that they introduce an extra piece of material into the circuit, which resists the flow of electricity. Explain that *resistance* means *acting against*.

Activities

 Do not use rechargeable batteries – they could overheat.

● Ask the children if a thinner wire in a circuit will affect the brightness of a bulb. They could find out by replacing the wires with fuse wire of different thicknesses. Ensure that bare wires do not touch, otherwise there will be a short circuit. The children could measure the brightness of the bulb and record their results on a graph (see topics 37 and 38). Discuss any surprises and help them to explain their results. ***Photocopiable sheet 13*** introduces a variable resistor made from a pencil 'lead' (graphite) – a conductor with greater resistance than the wire in the circuit.

Higher-achieving children
They could investigate the effects on a buzzer or bell of changing the length or thickness of the wire in the circuit. Use a sound sensor and datalogger to measure and record the volume of the bell or buzzer and present the results as a graph.

Lower-achieving children
They could first observe the effects of resistors (volume knobs) on everyday equipment, such as radios and cassette players. Draw out that when the knob is turned, the power is reduced or increased and so the volume is lowered or increased.

Plenary session

◆ Ask the children what happened to thin wires in a circuit. *Did they become hot?* Draw out that this means that energy was being produced. *How did this affect the bulb? How did it affect a bell or buzzer?*

Vocabulary

bell, brightness, bulb, buzzer, circuit, conduct, dimmer, electron, resistance, resistor, variable resistor, volt, voltage, volume

Changing circuits

40 Circuit symbols

Background information

Circuit diagrams use straight lines for wires which are not straight. Some children might find the diagrams easier to relate to circuits if they arrange the wires in a similar format.

Starting point

■ Ask the children what the difference is between a drawing and a diagram. Explain that a drawing is intended to look like the object, or objects, it represents, whereas a diagram uses symbols. Show them the drawing of a circuit on **Photocopiable sheet 14** and provide three different electrical circuits, one of which is the same as the drawing. Invite a volunteer to point out the one which matches the drawing and ask the others to check if this is correct. Invite them to compare the diagram with the drawing and to identify the symbols for wires, a bulb and a 1.5V cell.

Using the pictures

❑ Ask the children to identify the symbols used in the diagrams they have just looked at. Draw out the way in which 1.5V cells are represented. *What do the children notice about the symbol for a 3V battery?* (Two 1.5V cells.) Ask them if they can work out the symbol for a 4.5V and a 6V battery. A clue is that every 1.5 volts are represented using the symbol for a 1.5V cell. They need to use mathematics to work out how many 1.5V cells make up each battery.

❑ Show the children a circuit consisting of a bulb, a 1.5V cell and a switch, and ask them to draw a circuit diagram to represent it. Ask them to add a bulb to the circuit (in series) and to draw a diagram to represent the circuit.

QCA links

The children learn that there are conventional symbols for components in circuits and that these can be used to draw diagrams of circuits. They learn that these diagrams can be understood by anyone who knows the symbols and can be used to give instructions for constructing circuits. (QCA Unit 6G)

Activities

● **Photocopiable sheet 14** provides an introduction to circuit diagrams by giving an example of a drawing and a diagram of the same circuit for the children to compare. The children are then asked to make some circuits, which are presented as diagrams. They should use the key provided in the picture in the Photo Book.

● Ask the children to draw diagrams of other circuits they have made in previous lessons, based on their drawings of circuits and using what they have learned about circuit diagrams to help them, and then to swap with a partner, whose task is to make the circuit.

 Do not use rechargeable batteries – they could overheat.

Higher-achieving children

They could draw diagrams for circuits, incorporating a buzzer or a bell, a light and a switch; predict how they will work; and then build and test them. Encourage them to make a note of any problems and how they tried to solve them. *Did their solutions work?*

Lower-achieving children

Provide the components shown in each circuit diagram on the **Photocopiable sheet 14**, and help the children to set them out, as shown in the diagram, before connecting them.

Plenary session

◆ Discuss the advantages of using circuit diagrams with symbols instead of drawing pictures of circuits.

Vocabulary

battery, bell, brightness, bulb, buzzer, cell, circuit, diagram, fuse wire, motor, resistor, switch, symbol

41 Special switches

Photo Book reference Page 44

QCA links
The children explain observations in terms of knowledge about electrical circuits. They have opportunities to develop their knowledge of circuit symbols and of using diagrams to represent circuits they design. (QCA Unit 6G)

Background information

A photo sensor (light sensor) is an automatic switch which responds to the amount of light which hits it. Once the brightness of the light falls below a specific level, the sensor switches the circuit on – usually to operate a light. Other sensors respond to factors such as sound, heat and movement.

Starting points

■ Ask the children what a switch does in an electrical circuit. *How does it turn a light on or off, or sound a bell or buzzer?* Review their understanding that a switch can join or break a circuit.

■ Ask them to describe some of the different switches they have used and how they are operated: for example, flick, knife, rocker, pull and push switches. *Which type of switch is best for a doorbell, and why? Which ones are the best for lights, and why?*

Using the pictures

❏ Ask the children where they think this light is used. Ask them to write labels for different parts of the light on removable adhesive stickers, and to fix them to it. *Which part of the light glows when it is switched on? How is this similar to, and different from, other lights they have used?*

❏ Ask the children what they think the cylindrical-shaped device below the light is for. The illustration to the left of the photograph should give them a clue. Discuss what a sensor is for and how it is useful. Explain that this light has two sensors: a photo sensor (light sensor) which switches the light on in the dark, but only if the other sensor (an infrared motion sensor) responds to something moving within its range. For the light to shine, both sensors have to switch on (i.e. when something large enough to activate it moves into range and the light level around it is low). This light also has a switch which can be used to turn it on when only one or neither of these conditions applies.

Activities

● Ask the children to work in pairs or small groups to plan how to make and test a circuit in which a 'security light' is switched on by a photo sensor. Ask them to draw a picture of their planned circuit, draw a circuit diagram of it, using the symbols shown in topic 40 and to write an explanation of how it will work. Let them test their circuits and encourage them to make any necessary adjustments.

Higher-achieving children
They could add an override switch to their circuit so that it can be switched on when the conditions are not dark enough to operate the sensor.

Lower-achieving children
They could first make a simple circuit with a light and a switch. Ask them which part of the circuit they should replace to make the light switch on automatically in the dark.

Plenary session

◆ Draw out that the sensors used in security lights are special types of switch.

Vocabulary

brightness, bulb, circuit, diagram, light sensor, photo sensor, security light, switch, symbol

Photo Book reference Page 45

42 Switches in parallel

QCA links
The children use circuit symbols and diagrams to represent circuits they design. They have opportunities to suggest a question to investigate. (QCA Unit 6G))

Background information

Switches in parallel are used in domestic lighting systems where a light needs more than one switch: for example, in a hall and landing or any room with two or more entrances.

Starting points

- Ask the children if any lights in their homes have more than one switch. *Why? How do they think the switches are connected?*
- Ask them to draw a picture of a circuit they could make for a light on the landing of a model house. They could also draw a circuit diagram. Provide electrical components, from which they can choose the ones they need.
- Most children faced with this task make a circuit with two switches in series – both switches have to be on for the lamp to work:

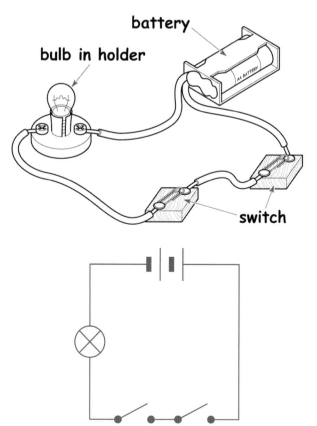

- Discuss why a circuit of this type would not work for a landing light. Explain that this is a series circuit, and tell the children that they are going to look at another way of putting two switches in a circuit. Children who have completed topic 41 and made a circuit for a security light with two switches might be able to suggest what to do.

Using the pictures

- ❑ *Did any children make a circuit like this?* Ask them how it is different from a series circuit. *How could it work for a landing light?*
- ❑ Can they make a light with three switches for a room with three entrances?

Activities

- The children could work in groups to make a model room from a box. Ask them to include a light which can be switched on from three different entrances.

Higher-achieving children
Challenge them to design a room in which two lights can each be switched on from three different entrances.

Lower-achieving children
They might need to spend some time investigating why switches in series do not always enable the user to switch a light on or off with one switch. (If either switch is off the light is off and the other switch has no effect.)

Plenary session

- ◆ Encourage the children to describe what happens when switches are in series and parallel. They could complete sentences such as, *If switch 'A' is switched off when switch 'B' is on …, If switch 'A' is switched on when switch 'B' is on …'*

Vocabulary

bulb, circuit, diagram, parallel, series, switch, symbol

Photo Book reference Page 46

43 Burglar alarms

QCA links
The children have an opportunity to use their scientific knowledge to identify significant features of an artefact to be designed. (QCA Unit 5/6H)

Background information

The components in the photographs can be used in a system which is linked remotely (ie, without wires) to a control box and a siren; but the components of burglar alarm systems can also be linked by wires. Sensors, of the types shown, are now more common than pressure-pad switches – which are easier for the children to make.

Starting point

- Ask the children if they have a burglar alarm at home. Ask them about the parts of it which can be seen (introduce the word *components*). *What would happen if a burglar broke in?*

Using the pictures

- Ask the children to discuss the burglar alarm components in the photographs; describe them and explain what they do, and explain how they show if a burglar has broken in.
- Invite feedback, and ask what other components the alarm is likely to have: for example, door sensors, a siren or bell, a flashing light and a control box.
- Draw out that these components have the same function – to switch on the siren or bell. Explain that they are not linked by wires but send remote signals to the control box using radio waves.

Activities

- Remind the children of switches they have made in lessons on electrical circuits: for example, from soft wood, drawing pins and paperclips. Ask them what a switch does in order to switch on a buzzer, bell or light (it joins a gap in a circuit).
- Challenge them to design a switch which completes a circuit when it is pushed and breaks the circuit when it is released. Provide materials to help them to try out their ideas: folded card, metal foil, paper fasteners, foam rubber, wires, buzzers and batteries.
- Ask them to make their switch to be hidden under a carpet so that it switches on a buzzer if someone treads on it.

Higher-achieving children
They could add a switch to the circuit for setting the alarm so that the buzzer or bell will operate only when this and the pressure pad switch are on. To do this, the switches need to be in series, not parallel (see topic 42).

Lower-achieving children
Remind them that there has to be a complete metal path for a circuit to work. Show how a piece of folded card can be covered with foil to make a switch which is operated by pressure and turns off when the pressure is removed:

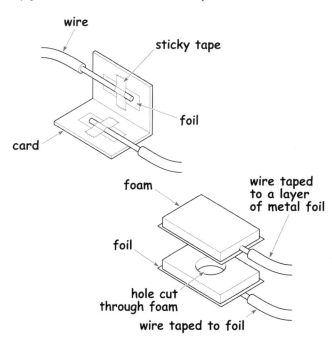

Different ways of making pressure pad switches.

Plenary session

- Ask the children to show their designs for burglar alarms and to say which they think works best in a specific place and why.

Vocabulary

burglar alarm, component, parallel, pressure pad, remote, sensor, series, switch, wire

Photo Book reference *Page 47*

44 Fuses

QCA links
The children have an opportunity to use their scientific knowledge to identify significant features of an artefact. (QCA Unit 5/6H)

Background information

The pin connected to the earth wire in an electric plug is linked directly to a water pipe, or other metal object, which leads to the ground. This enables electricity to run to earth, thereby protecting users from an electric shock if a fault develops in a cable or appliance. If there is a fault, excessive current may flow, causing overheating and, possibly, a fire. Current from the mains flows through the fuse to the appliance. The fuse is a thin wire within a glass or ceramic cartridge which can carry a stated current. A greater current makes the fuse melt, breaking the circuit and protecting the appliance by cutting it off from the electricity supply.

Starting points

■ The children should first have completed topic 39. Ask them about the effects of changing the thickness of the wires in a circuit. *What happened when they used thinner wires, and why?* Discuss what made the bulb dimmer and draw out that thin wire provides greater resistance to the flow of the electric current than does thick wire.

■ Discuss what happened to thinner wires in a circuit. If necessary, make a circuit with a bulb, battery and thin wires, such as fuse wire. The children should be able to feel that the wires heat up (at this low voltage they will not be dangerously hot).

Using the pictures

❑ Ask the children to look at the first picture to find out what fuses look like. Tell them that each fuse has a thin wire running though it. *How does the current reach this wire?* Draw out that the ends of the fuse casing are made of metal.

❑ Ask them to look at the photograph of fuse wires. *What can they find out about fuse wires from this? What does this picture tell them about the fuses?* Draw out that fuse wire is made in different thicknesses, and that fuses contain wire of different thicknesses. Ask: *What difference does the thickness of the wire make?*

❑ Explain the wiring of the electric plug. The brown wire is Live; it carries a live current to the appliance.

The blue wire is Neutral and the green and yellow is Earth (see Background information).

❑ *Can the children find the fuse in the picture of the plug?* Help them to follow the path of the electrical current through the plug (from the socket). Ask: *Into what might the electrical current flow from the plug?* Examples include a computer, kettle, heater or lamp. Point out that the fuse is part of the circuit and that it is positioned between the supply from the plug and the electrical appliance (such as a kettle or computer). Ask: *What happens to the fuse when the appliance is switched on?* Explain this (see Background information).

Activities

● The activities in topic 45 provide opportunities for the children to find out more about fuses and to build a fuse into a safe circuit.

Higher-achieving children
They could find other ways of short-circuiting a bulb or buzzer, and build in a fuse to prevent the battery overheating. They could find out about the fuses which should be used in connection with various appliances.

 Do not use rechargeable batteries. Remind the children of their previous learning about the dangers of experimenting with mains electricity.

Lower-achieving children
If necessary, review their previous learning about the effects of using thin wires in a circuit.

Plenary session

◆ Explain that fuses are safety devices which cut off the electricity supply to a device when they melt.

Vocabulary

appliance, circuit, current, earth, fuse, live, mains, neutral, plug, short circuit, socket

Photo Book reference *Page* 48

45 Short circuits

QCA links
The children have an opportunity to use their scientific knowledge to identify significant features of an artefact. (QCA Unit 5/6H)

Background information

Electricity generally follows the path which offers the lowest resistance. If it can flow around a circuit without doing any work, it does so; this causes the wires in the circuit to become hot and could lead to a fire.

Starting point

■ The children should first have completed topic 44. They might have heard adults at home talking about fuses which have 'blown'. Ask: *What does this mean?* Show them some pieces of wire of the type used in domestic appliances and some pieces of fuse wire. *What difference can the children see?* Discuss why the wires used for devices such as an electric iron or kettle are much thicker than those the children use in their investigations. (Domestic systems have a much more powerful circuit; they operate at 220 to 240 volts, whereas the cells and batteries used at school provide 1.5 to 6 volts.)

Using the pictures

❑ Ask the children to look at the first picture and circuit diagram, and to match the components in the circuit diagram to those in the picture. Ask them what will happen when the bulb is switched on. *What do they think they will see? What will they feel if they touch different parts of the circuit?*

❑ Repeat the above for the second circuit and ask the children how this is different from the first one. *What will happen when the bulb is switched on?*

Activities

● Provide electrical components from which the children can make the first circuit. The fuse should be made from a piece of wire wool. Ask them to record their observations. Ask: *What happens to the fuse, and why?* (It should become hotter than the rest of the wire in the circuit because it has a higher resistance, but it should not burn through). Ask them to indicate the path followed by the electrical current (from the negative battery terminal, along the wire, through the

switch, fuse and bulb, and back to the battery through the positive terminal.

● Before the children add the wire to connect the two attachments of the bulb, ask them if this will make any difference to the path followed by the electrical current.

● Ask them if it will pass through the bulb, the extra wire, or both. Let them add this wire and record their observations.

● Adding the wire to cause a short-circuit makes the fuse burn through; this can be quite spectacular.

● Ask the children to show the path followed by the current. *Did the bulb light? Did the current go through the bulb? Where did it go?*

 Warn the children to keep their faces and hands away from the fuse when they add the short circuit – or do it as a demonstration.

Higher-achieving children
They could make the circuit from the diagram only (mask the picture).

Lower-achieving children
Make a copy of the picture of the circuits. Ask the children to indicate with their fingers, and then add arrows, to show the path followed by the electricity when the circuits are switched on.

Plenary session

◆ Ask the children what happened to the fuse. *What made it burn through?* Discuss how this makes a circuit safe.

Vocabulary

circuit, component, diagram, fuse, mains, negative, positive, resistance, short circuit, terminal

Fertilisers

What differences do fertilisers make to plants?

- Plan a fair test to find out.

 Wash your hands after handling fertiliser, plants and soil.

You need
- **2 potted plants of the same kind: for example, geranium, busy lizzie, chrysanthemum**
- **plant fertiliser**
- **measuring cylinder or jug**

What we shall do	Other equipment needed
Things to keep the same	**What we shall change**
What we shall observe and measure	**How we shall record these observations and measurements**

Old mould

- Find out about the conditions which help mould to grow on bread.

- Put a piece of bread into a container and observe it each day for 2 weeks.

You could put a lid on the container or leave it open. You could put it in a fridge or freezer or leave it in a warm place.

you need
- a piece of bread
- a transparent or opaque plastic box with a lid
- a fridge or freezer

- Record your observations.

- Share your results with others.

Container	Lid or no lid	Place	Growth of mould (✓)													
			Days													
			1	2	3	4	5	6	7	8	9	10	11	12	13	14

Vaccine report

- Find out about the vaccines which have been developed for different diseases.

Use information books and the Internet

- Use this page to help you to plan a report about them.

Who developed the vaccine?

How?

When?

For which groups of people?

Where?

How was it tested?

The vaccine (against which disease)	The scientists
Date	Place

Why the scientists looked for a vaccine for this disease

Work on the vaccine (development and trials)

The people the vaccine helps	The difference it has made to the world

Yeast

- Find out what makes yeast grow.

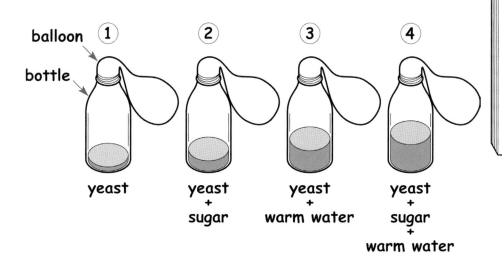

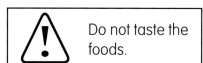

you need
- dried yeast
- sugar
- warm water
- 4 small bottles
- 4 balloons
- teaspoons

- Put the bottles somewhere warm.

- Record your observations on the chart.

⚠ Do not taste the foods.

Bottle	After 10 minutes	After 20 minutes	After 30 minutes
1. yeast			
2. yeast + sugar			
3. yeast + warm water			
4. yeast + sugar + warm water			

Now try this

- Repeat the investigation, using cold water.

- Put the bottles in a cold place.

A scientific discovery

● Write the answers on the grid.
  If they are all correct, the name of a piece of equipment used by Alexander Fleming will appear in the shaded column.

1. What did the mould which grew while Fleming was on holiday come from?
2. What name did Fleming give to the chemical in the mould?
3. What was Fleming hoping to make to use on wounds to prevent infections?
4. What caused the infections?
5. What kind of microbes does penicillin kill?
6. What type of living organism produces penicillin?
7. Soldiers in World War I were more likely to die from what, than from their wounds?
8. What name did Fleming give to the weak antiseptic which he found in many body fluids?
9. Alexander Fleming worked in the bacteriology laboratory of a _____ .

Write one letter in each box.

Teacher Note: See Resources (page 64) for answers. If necessary, insert some of the letters as clues.

54   *Accessing... SCIENCE* Teacher Resource Book Year 6   © Folens (copiable page)

Dissolve it

How can you make sugar dissolve more quickly?

● Write your ideas on the sugar bag.

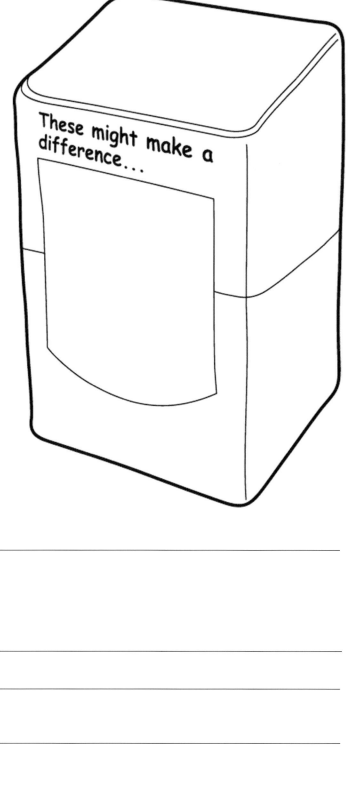

These might make a difference...

Which one will you test?

_____

What will you do?

_____

_____

_____

_____

What will you observe, count or measure?

_____

What will you keep the same?

_____

_____

What will you change?  _____

How will you know if your idea worked?

_____

_____

_____

_____

Solar still

● Follow the instructions to make a solar still.

You need
- a trowel or small spade
- a washing-up bowl
- rubber or plastic gloves
- 4 large stones
- a small stone
- a sack of dry leaves or grass
- a sheet of polythene about 120cm x 120cm

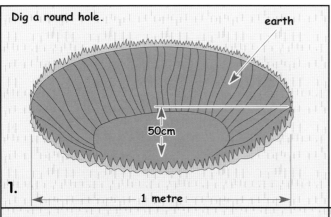

Dig a round hole.

earth

50cm

1 metre

1.

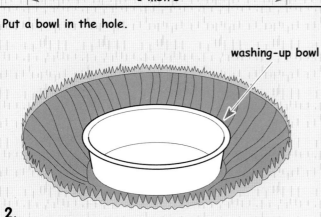

Put a bowl in the hole.

washing-up bowl

2.

Pack leaves or grass around the bowl up to 2cm from the top of the bowl.

3.

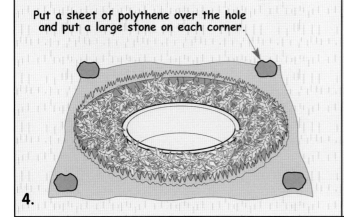

Put a sheet of polythene over the hole and put a large stone on each corner.

4.

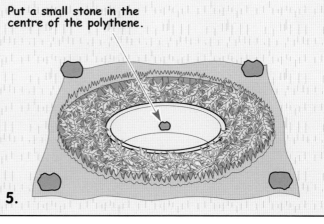

Put a small stone in the centre of the polythene.

5.

What happened?

_____

Explain how this happened.

_____

_____

_____

Where does the water come from?

What makes the water clean?

Fizz

Rainwagter is slightly acid.

● Find out how weak acids affect materials.

- – Put a little of the material into a jar.

- – Add some water.

- – Put on the lid.

- – Shake the jar.

- – Repeat this using white vinegar instead of water.

You need
- ● water
- ● white vinegar (an acid)
- ● marble chippings, glass marbles, limestone chippings, sand, washing soda, pieces of bone and teeth
- ● small jars with lids

● Record your observations.

Material	Observations	
	Mixed with water	Mixed with vinegar

Separate it

How can you separate all the materials in the mixture?

● Write your plan on the flow chart.

You need
● a mixture of beads, sand, salt and iron filings
● a sieve
● water
● a funnel and filter paper
● a shallow dish or saucer
● a magnet wrapped in paper or cling film

1.

This separates the

_____

because

_____

2.

This separates the _____

because _____

_____

_____

3.

This separates the _____

because _____

_____

_____

4.

This separates the _____

because _____

_____

_____

Central heating flow chart

You need
- the pictures from topic 25

- Complete the flow chart to describe the changes which happen in a central heating system.

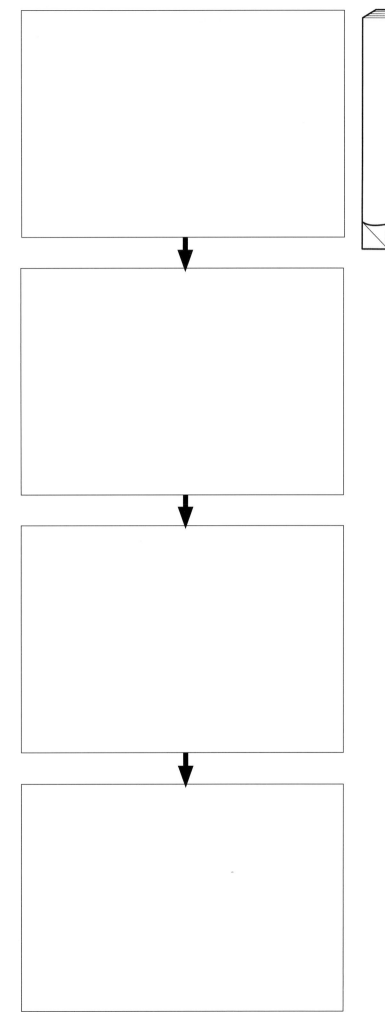

- List the changes which take place. _____

- What new materials are made? _____

Water away

- Find out how much water is displaced by objects of the same size but different masses.

- Weigh the cans.

- Record this on the chart.

- Collect the water each can displaces:

You need
- an empty soft drink can
- a drink can of the same size, full of sand
- a drink can of the same size, about half-filled with sand
- a drink can of the same size, about a quarter-filled with sand
- water
- a bucket
- a bowl
- measuring cylinder or jug
- scales

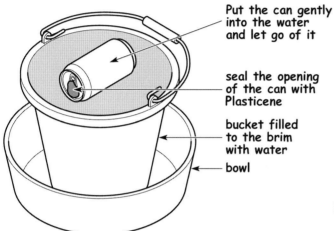

Put the can gently into the water and let go of it

seal the opening of the can with Plasticene

bucket filled to the brim with water

bowl

Do not push the cans under the water.

- Measure the volume of the displaced water.

- Weigh the displaced water.

- Record your results on the chart.

Can	Mass (g)	Volume of displaced water (cm³)	Mass of displaced water (g)	Did the can float?
Empty				
Full of sand				
Half-filled with sand				
Quarter-filled with sand				

- What pattern do you notice in your results?

- Write a rule about the weight of water which floating objects displace.

- Test your rule using other objects which float.

Kaleidoscope images

- Join 2 mirrors with tape.

- Stand the mirrors on the lines below.

- Put a counter or other small object on the spot.

- How many counters can you see?

- Remove the mirrors and measure the angle between the lines.

You need

- **2 plane mirrors**

- **masking tape**

- **protractor**

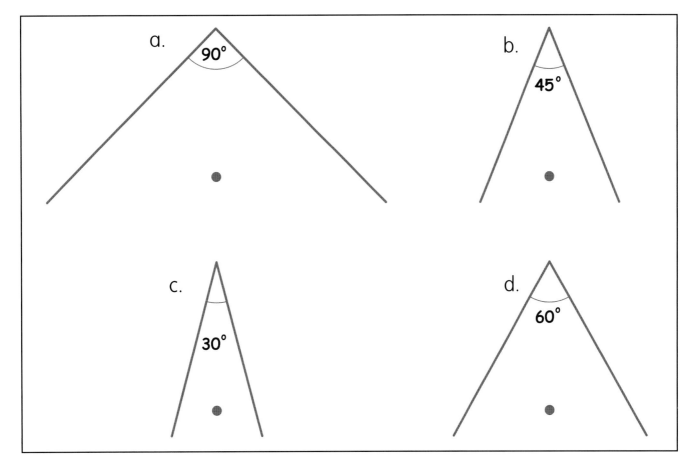

	Angle between mirrors	Number of counters
a		
b		
c		
d		

A complete revolution = 360°.

What pattern do you notice about the angle between the mirrors and the number of images?

_____

Circuit changers

- Make a circuit with a bulb and battery like this:

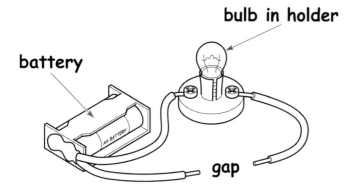

bulb in holder

battery

gap

You need
- a battery
- a bulb in a holder
- 3 wires
- a pencil sliced in half, lengthways
- a ruler
- small pieces of thin paper

- Put a pencil in the gap and join the wires to the pencil lead, like this:

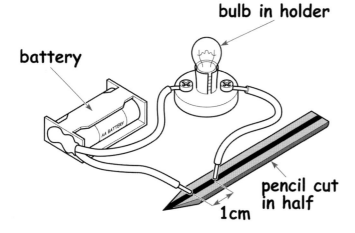

bulb in holder

battery

pencil cut in half

1cm

What happens?

_____

_____

_____

_____

- Measure the brightness of the bulb.

You could count the number of sheets of thin paper through which the bulb shines.

- Repeat this with different lengths of pencil lead between the wires.

- Record your results:

Distance between wires	Brightness of bulb (number of sheets of thin paper)
1cm	
2cm	
4cm	
8cm	
16cm	

Explain your results. _____

_____

Circuits and symbols

A circuit

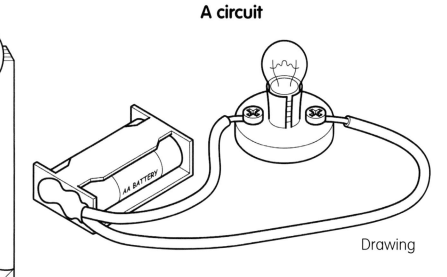

Drawing

You need
- 3 × 1.5V bulbs, in holders
- 3 × 1.5V cells and battery holders
- wire
- battery snaps
- a motor
- a buzzer
- a pencil sliced in half, lengthways
- 2 switches

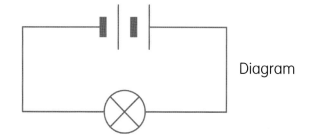

Diagram

- Make these circuits and record them as drawings:

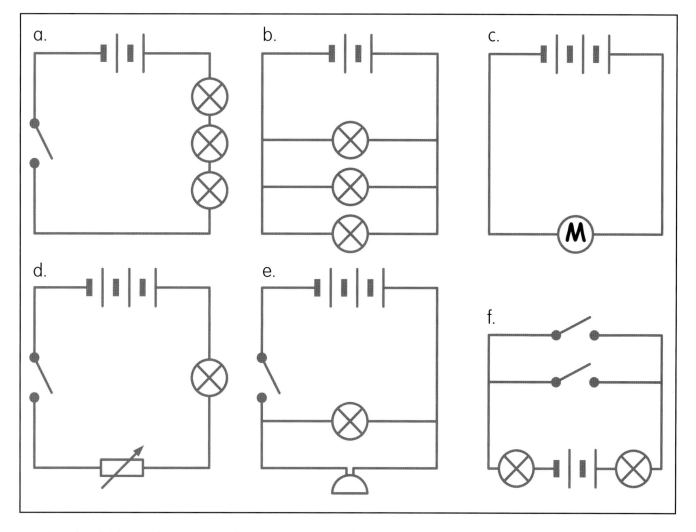

a.

b.

c.

d.

e.

f.

Resources

Interdependence and adaptation

Identifying plants. This site provides a list of questions to help you to identify a plant. Higher-attaining children could use it if they have made careful observations of a plant. http://www.reticule.co.uk/flora/content/SEARCH.ASP

Nature Trail Book of Trees, Malcolm Hart, Sue Tarsky, Ingrid Selberg, Su Swallow & Ruth Thomson, 1990, Usborne, *The Complete Guide to Trees,* Alan Mitchell & David More, 1985, Parkgate Books

Arum plant http://www.news.wisc.edu/titanarum/, http://www.rbgsyd.gov.au/conservation_research/horticulture_research/titan_arum/titan_arum_fact_sheet

Surtsey http://www.vulkaner.no/n/surtsey/esurtmenu.html

Deserts http://mbgnet.mobot.org/sets/desert/plants2.htm

Micro-organisms

Yeast (how yeast is made, how it is used in baking, bread recipes) http://www.breadworld.com/sciencehistory/science.asp

Mushrooms *The Kingfisher Guide to the Mushrooms and Toadstools of Britain and Europe,* David Pegler, Kingfisher, 1998, http://www.tastymushroompartnership.co.uk/, http://www.bioimages.org.uk/HTML/R141670.HTM, http://www.backyardnature.net/mushroom.htm

Reed beds http://www.hdra.org.uk/factsheets/fr5.htm

Influenza (Department of Health) http://www.dh.gov.uk/PolicyAndGuidance/HealthAndSocialCareTopics/Flu/fs/en

(National Health Service) http://www.nhsdirect.nhs.uk/

BBC Health http://www.bbc.co.uk/health/conditions/flu.shtml

More about dissolving

Drinking water http://www.environment-agency.gov.uk/ (Click on 'Water quality' and, for information from water authorities, 'Regional information'.)

Reversible and irreversible changes

Fire safety http://www.firekills.gov.uk/, http://www.odpm.gov.uk/stellent/groups/odpm_control/documents/contentservertemplate/odpm_index.hcst?n=3970&l=4

Forces in action

Finding Out About Sun, Moon and Planets (Lynn Myring & Sheila Snowden, Usborne)

NASA (activities and research for children) http://kids.msfc.nasa.gov/

BBC science (activities and information for children, including an interactive simulation of the rotation of the Earth and the Moon and the Earth's orbit around the Sun) http://www.bbc.co.uk/schools/scienceclips/ages/9_10/earth_sun_moon.shtml

Mr Archimedes' Bath (Pamela Allen, Puffin)

Who Sank the Boat? (Pamela Allen, Puffin)

How we see things

Cats' eyes http://www.jenkins-ip.com/mym/spring2000/t_news01.htm

Battery-powered light boxes are available from TTS http://www.tts-group.co.uk and Hope Education http://www.hope-education.co.uk/.

Changing circuits

Light bulbs http://home.howstuffworks.com/light-bulb.htm

Sensors Robolab http://www.mooreed.com.au/products/robolab/intelligenthouse.htm

(an introduction to robotics and datalogging with a micro motor, lamp, light, sensor, and all components for building a house frame and working garage door)

Solution to word grid on *Photocopiable sheet 5* (page 54).

		1	S	P	O	R	E					
		2	P	E	N	I	C	I	L	L	I	N
		3	A	N	T	I	S	E	P	T	I	C
	4	M	I	C	R	O	B	E	S			
5	B	A	C	T	E	R	I	A				
	6	M	O	U	L	D						
		7	I	N	F	E	C	T	I	O	N	S
8	L	Y	S	O	Z	Y	M	E				
		9	H	O	S	P	I	T	A	L		